MATRIX METHODS IN ECONOMICS

This book is in the
ADDISON-WESLEY SERIES IN
BEHAVIORAL SCIENCES: QUANTITATIVE METHODS
Series Editor: FREDERICK MOSTELLER

MATRIX METHODS IN ECONOMICS

CLOPPER ALMON, JR., *Department of Economics, University of Maryland*

ADDISON-WESLEY PUBLISHING COMPANY

Reading, Massachusetts · Palo Alto · London · Don Mills, Ontario

PREFACE

Was grinsest du mir, hohler Schädel, her . . .
Ihr Instrumente freilich spottet mein
Mit Rad and Kämmen, Walz' und Bügel:
Ich stand am Tor, ihr solltet Schlüssel sein—

(Goethe)

What are you grinning down at me, hollow skull? . . .
You instruments, I'm sure, make fun of mine
With your wheel and gears, roller and rings:
I stood at the door, and you should be the key—

We come upon Faust as he looks up at his scientific equipment on the shelves above him. Were he a modern quantitative economist—we shall see that he well might be—then as he peered up into his mathematical cabinet he would see on the first shelf the heavy caldrons of elementary calculus and statistics. From the second shelf, there would grin down at him matrix inversion, multiple regression, the analysis of variance and covariance, Lagrangian multipliers, linear and nonlinear programming, and the characteristic values of matrices. Amid these essential implements of his trade would squat FORTRAN, like a bug with a human face and the self-contented, enigmatic smile of a sphinx. Finally, on the top shelf would lie a clutter of devices which employ and extend the second-shelf methods. Simultaneous equation estimation techniques, spectral analysis, canonical correlation, factor analysis, errors-in-variables techniques, and lags distributed hither and yon might all be found there. Were Faust also a mathematical economist —instead of just a quantitative researcher—he would then need another whole dusty roomful of theorems.

This book, however, is confined to a thorough explanation of those essential second-shelf devices. It assumes that the reader has mastered a

v

standard basic calculus book, including the chapters on partial differentiation, multiple integrals, and (for Chapter 7 of this book) differential equations. In statistics, this book is logically, but not, I fear, intuitively, self-contained. Reading a short elementary statistics text should precede taking up this one. This book should provide a firm foundation for the several good books about third-shelf econometrics or for books on mathematics and statistics which take the "pure math" approach. In this book we will prove all the theorems we use, but we will limit the subjects to those of greatest value in practical applications. Above all, *we will stress computations.*

When five years ago I began teaching a course on these second-shelf methods, I soon learned that there were several good books on the first- and third-shelf subjects, but that one was supposed to pick up the second-shelf topics, as I had, from four or five courses, a dozen books, a year or so spent around a computing laboratory, and the highly compressed summaries the authors of the third-shelf books condescended to put in their opening chapters or appendices. As I got into the course, I discovered that these topics did not make just a *potpourri*, but that they fitted together in a tight, logical, linear progression. Moreover, the logical order was happily also the order of importance, and each major step could be applied to economic problems. One could begin with the problem of interindustry analysis and develop for it the pivotal process of matrix inversion. Regression analysis provides further insight into this process, and the proof of the "best-linear-unbiased" properties of least squares affords practice in reading a discussion involving matrices. A slight addition to the pivotal process produces the simplex method of linear programming, which can be used to prove the existence of shadow prices. These can then be generalized to the Lagrangian multipliers, which play so large a role in economic theory. The Lagrangian multipliers, in turn, become the means for proving the fundamental principal axes theorem on the characteristic vectors of symmetric matrices. Applications of this theorem involve the multivariate normal distribution and the analysis of variance and covariance, and lead into the characteristic values and vectors of nonsymmetric matrices. Here a new sort of pivot operation leads to the very soul of the matrix, its characteristic polynomial.

So the material all ties together.

Furthermore, I found that the theory did not have to be built up in one way, and then an entirely different set of ideas introduced for efficient computation. Instead, efficient computing schemes can carry the theoretical developments. This fact led to the exclusion of determinants from the text and to the inclusion of the chapter on FORTRAN programming. Learning FORTRAN is not only valuable in itself, but it makes possible a new way of studying the theory. I find that, more than any other task, writing a program leads a student to a close examination and a thorough understanding of a method.

From these ideas, for which I claim no originality, and from five years of teaching based upon them comes this book. It grew from notes used in a one-semester course for first-year graduate students at Harvard. Nearly all the material has been through the classroom test, though never all in the same semester. To the many students there who corrected, improved, and complained about four previous versions, I am most grateful. If at times it seems to you that the "wheels and gears, rollers and rings" are making fun of your head, do not loose heart; all your predecessors survived when the going was rougher.

On the other hand, do not suppose that these techniques will take the place of economic understanding and reveal to you the nature of the economy. They measure as blindly as does a scale. If nothing is on the scale but steak, you pay only for the steak. But if the butcher's hand is on also, you pay for that too. Since Adam Smith, we have known that the economy is full of invisible hands. The question is more often "what are we measuring?" than "what is the measurement?" Mechanical techniques are of little help on that fundamental question. That is what Faust was saying when we interrupted, and we would do well to listen:

Ich stand am Tor, ihr solltet Schlüssel sein
Zwar euer Bart ist kraus, doch hebt ihr nicht die Riegel.
Geheimnisvoll am lichten Tag
Lässt sich Natur des Schleiers nicht berauben,
Und was sie deinem Geist nicht offenbaren mag,
Das zwingst du ihr nicht ab mit Hebeln und mit Schrauben.

I stood at the door and you should be the key
Though deftly wrought, you do not lift the bolt.
Full of mystery in the light of day,
Nature will not be robbed of her veil
And what she will not manifest to your spirit
You won't force out of her with crowbars and gimlets.

Cambridge, Massachusetts   C.A., Jr.
June 1966

CONTENTS

*Starred sections may be omitted without loss of continuity.

CHAPTER 1

LINEAR EQUATIONS AND MATRICES

1-1 AN EXAMPLE OF A SYSTEM OF LINEAR EQUATIONS

In economic analysis and forecasting, it is often desirable to have more detailed information about the economy than broad aggregates such as Gross National Product offer. The behavior of the chemical industry may be very different from that of the steel industry or textile industry. For problems where these differences are important, the economy may be divided into a number of industries, which we shall number $1, 2, 3, \ldots, n$. The following problem then arises: Suppose that the final demands—that is, consumption, government, export, and capital investment demands—for the output of each industry are given. What then will the total outputs of the industries have to be in order for these final demands to be satisfied? For most industries, the total output must be greater than the final demand because other industries use some of the total output as intermediate products.

Let us denote the final demand for the products of industry j by b_j and the total output of that industry by x_j. We can answer the question posed above if we assume that the amount of product i used by industry j is proportional to the output of the latter:

$$\text{product } i \text{ used in industry } j = \alpha_{ij} x_j.$$

The total intermediate use of product i, the sum of its use by all industries, is then

$$\alpha_{i1} x_1 + \alpha_{i2} x_2 + \cdots + \alpha_{in} x_n.$$

Consequently, for the production of each industry to equal the total use of its products, the following equations must be satisfied:

$$\begin{aligned}
x_1 &= \alpha_{11} x_1 + \alpha_{12} x_2 + \cdots + \alpha_{1n} x_n + b_1, \\
x_2 &= \alpha_{21} x_1 + \alpha_{22} x_2 + \cdots + \alpha_{2n} x_n + b_2, \\
&\vdots \\
x_n &= \alpha_{n1} x_1 + \alpha_{n2} x_2 + \cdots + \alpha_{nn} x_n + b_n.
\end{aligned}$$

1

Example. Let us divide an imaginary economy into three sectors: (1) services, (2) manufacturing, and (3) agriculture, and let us measure the output of each of these industries in dollars. Now for every dollar's worth of output, the service industry requires 30 cents' worth of supplies from the manufacturing industry (in the form, perhaps, of office supplies, gasoline, automobile parts, medical preparations, and so on). That is to say, $\alpha_{21} = 0.30$. Similarly, for every dollar of its output, manufacturing consumes 33.3 cents' worth of services and 40 cents' worth of agricultural products, making $\alpha_{12} = 0.333$ and $\alpha_{32} = 0.40$. Finally, agriculture requires 16.7 cents of services (such as transportation) and 40 cents of manufactured products (fertilizers, gasoline, feed mixes) for each dollar of output. Table 1–1 summarizes these production relations.

Table 1–1

INPUT-OUTPUT COEFFICIENTS

Seller \ Buyer	1 Services	2 Manufacturing	3 Agriculture
1. Services	0.00	0.333	0.167
2. Manufacturing	0.30	0.000	0.400
3. Agriculture	0.00	0.400	0.000

If the final demands for the three sectors are 20, 48, and 14 billion dollars, respectively, the above equations then become

$$
\begin{aligned}
x_1 &= 0.00\, x_1 + 0.333\, x_2 + 0.167\, x_3 + 20, \\
x_2 &= 0.30\, x_1 + 0.000\, x_2 + 0.400\, x_3 + 48, \\
x_3 &= 0.00\, x_1 + 0.400\, x_2 + 0.000\, x_3 + 14.
\end{aligned}
\tag{1–1.1}
$$

We may write these equations somewhat more concisely by bringing to the left-hand side all terms that involve an x, as follows:

$$
\begin{aligned}
1.00\, x_1 - 0.333\, x_2 - 0.167\, x_3 &= 20, \\
-0.30\, x_1 + 1.000\, x_2 - 0.400\, x_3 &= 48, \\
0.00\, x_1 - 0.400\, x_2 + 1.000\, x_3 &= 14.
\end{aligned}
$$

Had our fancied economy had n sectors instead of only three, we would have ended up with a system of equations of this form:

$$
\begin{aligned}
a_{11}x_1 + a_{12}x_2 + \cdots + a_{1n}x_n &= b_1, \\
a_{21}x_1 + a_{22}x_2 + \cdots + a_{2n}x_n &= b_2, \\
&\;\;\vdots \\
a_{n1}x_1 + a_{n2}x_2 + \cdots + a_{nn}x_n &= b_n.
\end{aligned}
\tag{1–1.2}
$$

Comparing systems (1–1.1) and (1–1.2), we see that in (1–1.1), $n = 3$ and $a_{12} = -0.333$. What are the values of a_{21}, a_{32}, a_{11}, a_{23}, a_{31}, and a_{13}?

In mathematics, the set of equations shown in (1–1.2) is called a *system of simultaneous linear equations in n unknowns*. We shall see such systems arise in various ways in economics. When such a system represents, as in our example, interindustry supply requirements, it is called the Leontief *input-output* system.

Equations (1–1.2) are called "linear" by extension from the case where $n = 2$, for an equation of the form

$$a_{11}x_1 + a_{12}x_2 = b_1$$

shows a straight-line relationship between x_1 and x_2 when it is graphed.

In Section 1–3, we will develop a method of solving systems such as (1–1.1) for the x's. First, we must mention some concepts which are extremely useful in dealing with these systems.

1-2 NOTATION AND INTERPRETATIONS OF THE SOLUTION OF LINEAR EQUATIONS

In writing Eq. (1–1.2), it is time-consuming and tiresome to repeat the x_1, x_2, etc., and all the $+$ and $=$ signs so many times. Another, more economical, way of writing the equations is

$$x_1 \begin{pmatrix} a_{11} \\ \vdots \\ a_{n1} \end{pmatrix} + x_2 \begin{pmatrix} a_{12} \\ \vdots \\ a_{n2} \end{pmatrix} + \cdots + x_n \begin{pmatrix} a_{1n} \\ \vdots \\ a_{nn} \end{pmatrix} = \begin{pmatrix} b_1 \\ \vdots \\ b_n \end{pmatrix}. \qquad (1\text{–}2.1)$$

Equation (1–2.1) should be thought of as just another way of writing Eq. (1–1.2). The expressions

$$\begin{pmatrix} a_{11} \\ \vdots \\ a_{n1} \end{pmatrix}, \quad \begin{pmatrix} a_{12} \\ \vdots \\ a_{n2} \end{pmatrix}, \quad \text{etc.,} \quad \text{and} \quad \begin{pmatrix} b_1 \\ \vdots \\ b_n \end{pmatrix}$$

are called *vectors*, or sometimes *column vectors*, since their elements are arranged in columns. Since the vectors in (1–2.1) are to be thought of as mathematical objects in their own right, it is convenient to give them names such as a_1, a_2, ..., a_n, and b, respectively. The expression

$$x_1 a_1 \qquad \text{or} \qquad x_1 \begin{pmatrix} a_{11} \\ \vdots \\ a_{n1} \end{pmatrix}$$

is called the product of the scalar x_1 and the vector a_1, and is defined as

$$x_1 a_1 = x_1 \begin{pmatrix} a_{11} \\ \vdots \\ a_{n1} \end{pmatrix} = \begin{pmatrix} x_1 a_{11} \\ \vdots \\ x_1 a_{n1} \end{pmatrix}.$$

Adding two vectors means adding their corresponding components, as can be seen by comparing (1–2.1) with (1–1.2).

In this notation, the equations of the preceding numerical example can be written as

$$x_1 \begin{pmatrix} 1 \\ -0.3 \\ 0 \end{pmatrix} + x_2 \begin{pmatrix} -0.333 \\ 1 \\ -0.4 \end{pmatrix} + x_3 \begin{pmatrix} -0.167 \\ -0.4 \\ 1 \end{pmatrix} = \begin{pmatrix} 20 \\ 48 \\ 14 \end{pmatrix}.$$

If we can find $x_1, \ldots, x_n$ such that

$$x_1 a_1 + x_2 a_2 + \cdots + x_n a_n = b, \tag{1–2.2}$$

then b is said to be a *linear combination* of $a_1, a_2, \ldots, a_n$, with weights $x_1, \ldots, x_n$. Alternatively, the vector

$$x = \begin{pmatrix} x_1 \\ \vdots \\ x_n \end{pmatrix}$$

is said to *represent* the vector b relative to the vectors $a_1, a_2, \ldots, a_n$. In the input-output system, for example, the $x_1, \ldots, x_n$ are the outputs of the various industries, and it seems natural enough to speak of the outputs as "representing" the final demand relative to the producing activities of the various industries. We see then that the problem of finding a solution to (1–2.1), or to (1–2.2), can also be interpreted as "finding the representation of b relative to $a_1, \ldots, a_n$" or "finding the linear combination of $a_1, \ldots, a_n$ which is equal to b."

An additional interpretation comes from further abbreviation of the notation for (1–1.2). There are still unnecessarily many $+$ signs and parentheses in (1–2.1). Let us write it in an even simpler way:

$$\begin{pmatrix} a_{11} & a_{12} & \cdots & a_{1n} \\ a_{21} & a_{22} & \cdots & a_{2n} \\ \vdots & & & \vdots \\ a_{n1} & a_{n2} & \cdots & a_{nn} \end{pmatrix} \begin{pmatrix} x_1 \\ x_2 \\ \vdots \\ x_n \end{pmatrix} = \begin{pmatrix} b_1 \\ b_2 \\ \vdots \\ b_n \end{pmatrix}. \tag{1–2.3}$$

The array of the a_{ij} on the left-hand side of (1–2.3) is called a *matrix*. The horizontal lines of elements, such as $(a_{21}, a_{22}, \ldots, a_{2n})$, are called *rows* of the matrix; the vertical lines, such as

$$\begin{pmatrix} a_{12} \\ a_{22} \\ \vdots \\ a_{n2} \end{pmatrix},$$

are called *columns* of the matrix. This particular matrix is square; it has the same number of columns as rows. In general, the number of columns of a matrix does not have to equal the number of rows. We shall say that a matrix with n rows and m columns has dimensions (n, m) or, for short, is n by m. (The number of rows is mentioned first, just as in the subscripts on a_{ij}, the row subscript i comes first.)

In this matrix notation, the input-output example of Section 1-1 appears as

$$\begin{pmatrix} 1 & -0.333 & -0.167 \\ -0.3 & 1 & -0.4 \\ 0 & -0.4 & 1 \end{pmatrix} \begin{pmatrix} x_1 \\ x_2 \\ x_3 \end{pmatrix} = \begin{pmatrix} 20 \\ 48 \\ 14 \end{pmatrix}. \tag{1-2.4}$$

Since the matrix, like the vector, is to be thought of as an entity in its own right, it is natural to give it a name, say A. Then (1-2.3) may be written as

$$Ax = b. \tag{1-2.5}$$

This concise form is our ultimate shorthand for the cumbersome system (1-1.2). The vector x is said to be multiplied by the matrix A (or, more precisely, x is premultiplied by A). The meaning of multiplying a vector by a matrix is completely spelled out when we equate the left-hand sides of (1-2.5) and (1-1.2), or, in slightly greater generality, by the following summary equation:

$$Ax = \begin{pmatrix} a_{11} & a_{12} & \cdots & a_{1m} \\ a_{21} & a_{22} & \cdots & a_{2m} \\ \vdots & & & \vdots \\ a_{n1} & a_{n2} & \cdots & a_{nm} \end{pmatrix} \begin{pmatrix} x_1 \\ x_2 \\ \vdots \\ x_m \end{pmatrix}$$

$$= \begin{pmatrix} a_{11}x_1 + a_{12}x_2 + \cdots + a_{1m}x_m \\ a_{21}x_1 + a_{22}x_2 + \cdots + a_{2m}x_m \\ \vdots & & & \vdots \\ a_{n1}x_1 + a_{n2}x_2 + \cdots + a_{nm}x_m \end{pmatrix}. \tag{1-2.6}$$

Note that for the product Ax to be defined, it is *not* necessary that A and x have the same number of rows, but only that A have the same number of columns as x has rows.

Examples. The reader should check his understanding of the multiplication process by working through these examples:

$$\begin{pmatrix} 2 & 3 & 1 \\ -1 & 2 & 1 \\ 7 & -5 & 8 \end{pmatrix} \begin{pmatrix} 2 \\ 3 \\ -1 \end{pmatrix} = \begin{pmatrix} 12 \\ 3 \\ -9 \end{pmatrix},$$

$$\begin{pmatrix} 3 & 2 & 5 & 4 \\ -6 & 4 & -2 & 1 \end{pmatrix} \begin{pmatrix} 3 \\ 2 \\ 1 \\ 2 \end{pmatrix} = \begin{pmatrix} 26 \\ -10 \end{pmatrix}.$$

One can *add* two matrices, each having the same number of rows and the same number of columns, simply by adding corresponding elements.

Examples

$$\begin{pmatrix} 2 & 3 \\ 1 & 4 \end{pmatrix} + \begin{pmatrix} 8 & 4 \\ 7 & 1 \end{pmatrix} = \begin{pmatrix} 10 & 7 \\ 8 & 5 \end{pmatrix},$$

$$(3 \quad 2 \quad 5) + (5 \quad 4 \quad 2) = (8 \quad 6 \quad 7).$$

Observe that multiplying a vector by a matrix *transforms* the given vector into another vector. This transformation has two important properties:

If λ is a number, $\lambda(Ax) = A(\lambda x)$.   (1–2.7)

If x and y are two vectors, $A(x + y) = Ax + Ay$.   (1–2.8)

Proof. We can easily prove these rules by using the summation notation, Σ. This notation, like matrix and vector notation, is a shorthand. Thus, we use $\sum_{j=1}^{n} c_j$ as an abbreviation for the words, "the summation of the c_j, j going from 1 to n," or in symbols,

$$\sum_{j=1}^{n} c_j = c_1 + c_2 + c_3 + \cdots + c_n.$$

Assuming that x has n elements, the ith element of the vector on the left-hand side of (1–2.7) is $\lambda \sum_{j=1}^{n} a_{ij} x_j$, while the ith element of the vector on the right-hand side is $\sum_{j=1}^{n} a_{ij} \lambda x_j$. But

$$\lambda \sum_{j=1}^{n} a_{ij} x_j = \sum_{j=1}^{n} \lambda a_{ij} x_j = \sum_{j=1}^{n} a_{ij} \lambda x_j,$$

proving (1–2.7). Proof of (1–2.8) is left as an exercise.

A transformation of vectors with the properties (1–2.7) and (1–2.8) is said to be *linear*. Therefore, any matrix may be regarded as representing a linear transformation of vectors. And thus we come to a third interpretation of (1–1.2): Find the vector, x, which is transformed by A into the given vector, b.

A vector with two elements may be represented by a point in two-dimensional space. In Fig. 1–1, the point p corresponds to the vector $\binom{3}{2}$. Similarly, a vector with three elements corresponds to a point in three-dimensional space. By extension of this idea, we speak of a vector with n elements as a point in "n-dimensional space." By *n-dimensional space* is meant simply the set or collection of *all* vectors with n elements.

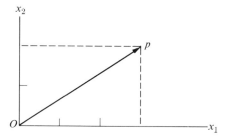

Figure 1–1

In plotting a two-dimensional vector, we customarily connect the point to the origin by an arrow, as shown in Fig. 1–1. In astronomy, the origin is the center of the solar system and the point is the position of a planet. The line between them can be thought of as the "carrier" or "bearer" of the revolving planet—hence the word "vector" from Latin *vectum*, past participle of *vehere*, to carry or bear, from which our word "vehicle" is also derived.

PROBLEMS

1. Find the products Ab, Ac, $A(2b + 3c)$, where

$$A = \begin{pmatrix} -1 & 4 & 1 \\ 2 & 3 & -4 \\ 3 & 1 & 2 \end{pmatrix}, \qquad b = \begin{pmatrix} 3 \\ 5 \\ 1 \end{pmatrix}, \qquad c = \begin{pmatrix} -2 \\ 4 \\ 2 \end{pmatrix}.$$

Verify that $A(2b + 3c) = 2(Ab) + 3(Ac)$.

2. Find $A + B$ and Bc, where A and c are as above and

$$B = \begin{pmatrix} 1 & 2 & 2 \\ 3 & -3 & 1 \\ 2 & 3 & 2 \end{pmatrix}.$$

Verify that $(A + B)c = Ac + Bc$.

3. Using the summation notation, prove Eq. (1–2.8).

1-3 SOLUTION OF EQUATIONS BY GAUSS-JORDAN ELIMINATION

We now come to a method of actually solving the system of Eq. (1-1.2). This method is not only the most useful for machine computation, but also fundamental to understanding much of the following theory. It is perhaps best shown by an example. Suppose we have the following set of equations:

$$3x_1 + 2x_2 + 6x_3 = 3, \tag{1-3.1}$$

$$1x_1 + 1x_2 + 4x_3 = 0, \tag{1-3.2}$$

$$2x_1 + 2x_2 + 6x_3 = 2. \tag{1-3.3}$$

For convenience in computing, these equations are rewritten in Tableau 0 of Table 1-2 with the x's, the $+$, and the $=$ signs omitted, though the x's are shown in the heading for reference. The right-hand side is called the "Constant column," and the fifth column in Table 1-2, labeled "Sum," is simply the sum of the elements in the first four columns. It is included only to check the arithmetic; it plays no role in the theory, and is omitted when there is no danger of arithmetic mistakes.

The plan of attack is now to use Eq. (1-3.1) to eliminate x_1 from Eqs. (1-3.2) and (1-3.3). We then use the modified Eq. (1-3.2), with x_1 eliminated, to eliminate x_2 from Eqs. (1-3.1) and (1-3.2). And lastly, we

Table 1-2

		x_1	x_2	x_3	Constant column	Sum
	(0.1)	3	2	6	3	14
Tableau 0	(0.2)	1	1	4	0	6
	(0.3)	2	2	6	2	12
	(1.1)	1	$\frac{2}{3}$	2	1	$4\frac{2}{3}$
Tableau 1	(1.2)	0	$\frac{1}{3}$	2	-1	$\frac{4}{3}$
	(1.3)	0	$\frac{2}{3}$	2	0	$\frac{8}{3}$
	(2.1)	1	0	-2	3	2
Tableau 2	(2.2)	0	1	6	-3	4
	(2.3)	0	0	-2	2	0
	(3.1)	1	0	0	1	2
Tableau 3	(3.2)	0	1	0	3	4
	(3.3)	0	0	1	-1	0

use the modified Eq. (1–3.3), with x_1 and x_2 eliminated, to eliminate x_3 from Eqs. (1–3.1) and (1–3.2). The basic facts used in these eliminations are:

a) If one of the equations is divided by a nonzero constant, the resulting system of equations has exactly the same solutions as the initial system.

b) If one of the equations is multiplied by a constant and added to another equation, the resulting system of equations has exactly the same solutions as the initial system. (If x satisfies two equations, it also satisfies their sum; equals added to equals are equal.)

The first step is to divide row (0.1) by 3 *to make the diagonal* element equal 1;* the result is written as row (1.1). Then multiply row (1.1) by 1 and subtract from row (0.2) to get row (1.2). Multiply row (1.1) by 2 and subtract from row (0.3) to get row (1.3). The object of these two operations is to eliminate x_1 from the second and third equations, or, in terms of the tableau, *to get a zero in all the off-diagonal positions of the first column.* (Observe that by performing the same operation on the sum column as on the other columns, we obtain a column in Tableau 1 whose elements should be equal to the sum of the elements in the corresponding rows of the first four columns. This column can, therefore, be used to check arithmetic.)

Proceeding to Tableau 2, we make the diagonal element in the second column equal to 1 by dividing row (1.2) by $\frac{1}{3}$. Then by subtracting a multiple of row (2.2) from the other rows, we get a zero in all the off-diagonal positions of the *second* column. The procedure is then repeated until all the off-diagonal elements are 0, and all the diagonal elements are 1. The answers are then simply read from the "Constant" column. In Table 1–2, they are $x_1 = 1$, $x_2 = 3$, $x_3 = -1$.

This method of solution is called *Gauss-Jordan elimination.* The process of going from one tableau to the next is called a *pivot* operation. The element on which the operation "turns," as it were, is naturally called the pivot element; in Table 1–2, these pivot elements are distinguished by squares drawn around them. The pivots are all diagonal elements.

The following processes are called *elementary row operations:*

a) multiplying one row of a matrix by a nonzero constant, i.e., multiplying each element of the row by the constant,

b) multiplying one row of a matrix by a constant and adding the result to another row, and

c) interchanging two rows, e.g., making the first row second and the second first.

Gauss-Jordan elimination is thus a sequence of elementary row operations; the need for (c) will be seen in the next section.

---

* The elements $a_{11}, a_{22}, \ldots, a_{nn}$ are called the diagonal of the matrix.

PROBLEMS

1. Solve the equation $Ax = b$, where

$$A = \begin{pmatrix} 2 & 4 & 6 \\ 4 & 10 & 6 \\ 6 & 13 & 10 \end{pmatrix}$$

and

$$b = \begin{pmatrix} 4 \\ 26 \\ 31 \end{pmatrix}.$$

Check the x-vector of your answer by multiplying it by A. Do you get b?

2. Solve the input-output system given by Eq. (1–1.1).

3. Use the data of Problem 2 to find the 2-by-2 input-output matrix for this economy, assuming that there is no final demand for services, and that manufacturing and agriculture each produce the services they require by using the technology shown in column 1. Note that the result is the same as the lower right two-by-two matrix found in Problem 2 after the first pivot operation. Develop this observation into an economic interpretation of the Gauss-Jordan elimination as applied to input-output matrices.

1–4 SINGULAR MATRICES AND LINEAR DEPENDENCE

The Gauss-Jordan elimination process works smoothly so long as we never have to divide by a zero. If, however, in, say, the $(i - 1)$-tableau, the element in the (i, i) position is zero, a straight application of the above procedure calls for division by zero and is impossible. The following two cases arise.

CASE I. Some element below the zero in the same column is not zero. The row (including the constant and sum columns) in which this nonzero element in the ith column occurs then changes places with row i in which the zero occurred in the pivot position. This row interchange certainly does not affect the solution of the system of equations; but, by putting a nonzero number in the pivot position, it allows the elimination to continue. Table 1–3 contains an example.

CASE II. All elements below the zero and in its columns are also zero. We will call this condition the "singularity signal," for in this case, the matrix is said to be *singular*, and the given equations either will have no solution or will have an infinite number of solutions—a somewhat "singular" circumstance! To see why the singularity signal indicates this absence or multiplicity of solutions, complete the Gauss-Jordan process, skipping the columns in which singularity signals occur. See the example in Table 1–4.

Table 1-3

x_1	x_2	x_3	Constant column
1	2	3	0
2	4	5	0
3	2	1	−4
1	2	3	0
0	→ 0	−1	0
0	−4	−8	−4

Interchange 2nd and 3rd equations

1	2	3	0
0	−4	−8	−4
0	0	−1	0
1	0	−1	−2
0	1	2	1
0	0	−1	0
1	0	0	−2
0	1	0	1
0	0	1	0

Table 1-4

	x_1	x_2	x_3	First constant column	Second constant column	Third constant column
R_1	2	4	6	8	8	0
R_2	3	6	5	8	8	0
R_3	4	8	4	0	8	0
$\frac{1}{2}R_1$	1	2	3	4	4	0
$R_2 - \frac{3}{2}R_1$	0	$\boxed{0}$	−4	−4	−4	0
$R_3 - 2R_1$	0	$\boxed{0}$	−8	−16	−8	0
		Singularity signal				
$-\frac{1}{4}R_1 + \frac{3}{8}R_3$	1	2	0	−2	1	0
$R_2 - \frac{1}{2}R_1 - \frac{1}{2}R_3$	0	0	0	4	0	0
$-\frac{1}{8}R_3 + \frac{1}{4}R_1$	0	0	1	2	1	0

In the final tableau, the row of the pivot element involved in the *last* singularity signal will be a row of zeros, for the Gauss-Jordan process or previous singularity signals have put zeros in all the off-diagonal positions, and the last signal gives a zero in the diagonal position. This row then gives an equation of the form

$$0x_1 + 0x_2 + \cdots + 0x_n = C. \tag{1–4.1}$$

If $C \neq 0$, clearly no $x_1, \ldots, x_n$ will satisfy this equation; hence, the system has no solution. The original equations were inconsistent. But if $C = 0$, any set of x's will satisfy the equation. The x_i corresponding to the column in which the last singularity signal appeared may be chosen arbitrarily and the other equations used to determine the remaining variables. To show these two possibilities, Table 1–4 gives two different constant columns. If the first column is the right-hand side of the equations, no solution is possible; if the second column is the right-hand side, an infinite number of solutions is possible. For example, if we set $x_2 = 1$, then $x_1 = -1$ and $x_3 = 1$; or if we set $x_2 = 2$, then $x_1 = -3$ and $x_3 = 1$; we could continue in this manner as long as we pleased.

Do singular matrices arise in economics? They do, and we can save considerable time and confusion by being able to recognize them readily. Theorem 1–5 provides a criterion which often allows us to spot such singular matrices without going through the elimination process. It will also show that singularity has nothing to do with the order in which the equations or variables are listed. An economic example follows Theorem 1–5.

Nonsingular matrices are, of course, matrices which are not singular.* From our previous discussion, we have

Theorem 1–1. If a matrix A is nonsingular, the equations $Ax = b$ have a unique solution for *any* vector b. If $b = 0$, then $x = 0$ (0 = vector of zeros).

We can now prove

Theorem 1–2. A matrix is singular if and only if one of its rows is a linear combination of other rows.

Proof. If the matrix is singular, that is, if it gives the singularity signal, a continuation of the elimination process will lead to a row of zeros in the final tableau. We derived this row of zeros by subtracting a linear combina-

---

* The addition of an arbitrarily small $\epsilon > 0$ to certain elements of a singular matrix makes it nonsingular. Thus, the singular matrices are isolated fellows, surrounded by "regular" or "nonsingular" ones. Hence the appellation "singular."

tion of the other original rows from the row that was originally there. Hence that original row was equal to that linear combination. (See the left-hand stub of Table 1–4, which expresses each row of each tableau as a linear combination of the original three rows, R_1, R_2, and R_3.) Conversely, if, say, the nth row is a linear combination of the first $n-1$ rows with weights $\lambda_1, \ldots, \lambda_{n-1}$, then we must have $b_n = \lambda_1 b_1 + \cdots + \lambda_{n-1} b_{n-1}$ if $Ax = b$ is to have a solution. Hence $Ax = b$ does *not* have a solution for *all* b and therefore, by Theorem 1–1, A is singular.

Theorem 1–3. If a matrix is singular, the equation $Ax = 0$ ($0 =$ vector of zeros) has a solution in which not all the x_i are zero, and therefore one column of A is a linear combination of the other columns.

Proof. The C in Eq. (1–4.1) is certainly zero, so we have an infinite number of solutions. (See the third constant column in Table 1–4.)

Theorem 1–4. If one column of a matrix is a linear combination of the other columns, then the matrix is singular.

Proof. It is then possible to find a solution to the equation $Ax = 0$ with $x \neq 0$. But $x = 0$ is also a solution, so the solution is not unique. Therefore, by Theorem 1–1, A must be singular.

If there exist numbers $\lambda_i, \ldots, \lambda_n$ not all equal to zero and such that $\lambda_1 a_1 + \cdots + \lambda_n a_n = 0$, where $a_1, \ldots, a_n$, and 0 are vectors, then the $a_1, \ldots, a_n$ are said to be *linearly dependent*. Vectors which are not linearly dependent are called *linearly independent*.

The preceding theorems may then be summarized by the following theorem:

Theorem 1–5. A matrix is nonsingular if and only if its rows are linearly independent, which is true if and only if its columns are linearly independent.

A set of n linearly independent n-dimensional vectors may be called a *basis* for n-dimensional space, for any other vector in the space can be expressed as a linear combination of them. This last statement is equivalent to Problem 2 below and is a consequence of Theorems 1–1 and 1–5.

A simple instance of a singular system arises in the following problem. We desire to know the coal input and the gas and oil input into each of the two sectors, ferrous and nonferrous metals, separately. That is, we wish to know x_1, x_2, x_3, and x_4 in Table 1–5. From one source of data, we know the total fuel use by each industry, shown at the bottom of the table; from another source, we know the use of each fuel by the two industries combined. Can we deduce the values of x_1, x_2, x_3, and x_4? We have four

Table 1–5

Consuming sector / Producing sector	Ferrous metals	Nonferrous metals	
Coal	x_1	x_2	80
Oil & Gas	x_3	x_4	40
Total	100	20	

equations in the four unknowns:

$$\begin{pmatrix} 1 & 1 & 0 & 0 \\ 0 & 0 & 1 & 1 \\ 1 & 0 & 1 & 0 \\ 0 & 1 & 0 & 1 \end{pmatrix} \begin{pmatrix} x_1 \\ x_2 \\ x_3 \\ x_4 \end{pmatrix} = \begin{pmatrix} 80 \\ 40 \\ 100 \\ 20 \end{pmatrix}.$$

Why not solve them for the unknowns? Because $R_4 = R_1 + R_2 - R_3$, where R_i is the ith row. Theorem 1–5 then informs us that the system is singular. No unique solution can be found, for one equation is redundant; it is implied by the others and gives no new information. The student of economic theory will recall a similar situation in the Walrasian theory of general equilibrium.

PROBLEMS

1. Show that the following matrix, A, is singular by expressing (a) one row as a linear combination of the other rows and (b) one column as a linear combination of the other columns.

$$A = \begin{pmatrix} 3 & -6 & 12 \\ 5 & -1 & 6 \\ 8 & 2 & 4 \end{pmatrix}.$$

Use Gauss-Jordan elimination and the arguments used in proving Theorems 1–2 and 1–3.

2. Show that no more than n n-dimensional vectors can be linearly independent.

3. The row *rank* of a matrix is the minimum number of rows from which all rows in the matrix can be produced by linear combination. Show that the row rank is equal to the number of nonzero rows in the final tableau of the reduction process. Replacing the word "rows" by "columns" in the definition of rank gives the definition of column rank. Show that for any matrix, the row rank equals the column rank. (Hence, the adjective is usually dropped, and one speaks simply of the rank of the matrix.)

1-5 THE INVERSE OF A MATRIX AND MATRIX MULTIPLICATION

It frequently happens that we wish to know the solution to a number of systems of equations, $Ax = b$, $Ax = c$, $Ax = d$, etc., all of which have the same nonsingular matrix on the left. We might, for example, wish to know the solution of a Leontief system for several different vectors of final demand, and we may not know all the vectors we will want to try when we first begin. Is there a way to lighten the work, to use the experience with one system to help us with another? The answer is, of course, yes; and the method is the use of the inverse matrix.

To define the inverse matrix of a given square matrix A, let us set up the equations

$$As_1 = e_1, \quad As_2 = e_2, \quad \ldots, \quad As_n = e_n, \tag{1-5.1}$$

where e_i is a vector with a 1 in its ith row, and zero everywhere else. (We shall use this notation repeatedly.) The matrix $S = (s_1, s_2, \ldots, s_n)$, that is, the matrix whose columns are s_1, s_2, etc., is called the *inverse* of the matrix A and is denoted by A^{-1}. If the inverse, S, of A is known, the solution of the equations $Ax = b$ may be found quickly. Indeed, it is simply $x = Sb$, for

$$
\begin{aligned}
A(Sb) &= A(b_1s_1 + b_2s_2 + \cdots + b_ns_n) \\
&\quad \text{(1-2.1), (1-2.5)} \\
&= b_1As_1 + b_2As_2 + \cdots + b_nAs_n \\
&\quad \text{(1-2.7), (1-2.8)} \\
&= b_1e_1 + b_2e_2 + \cdots + b_ne_n = b. \\
&\quad \text{(1-5.1)} \qquad\qquad\qquad \text{(1-2.4)}
\end{aligned}
\tag{1-5.2}
$$

The number(s) in parentheses below an equal sign indicates the equation(s) which justifies the equality. In the inverse notation, Eq. (1-5.2) may be summarized as follows:

Theorem 1-6. If A has an inverse A^{-1}, then the solution of

$$Ax = b \quad \text{is} \quad x = A^{-1}b. \tag{1-5.3}$$

Theorem 1-7. A square matrix has an inverse if and only if it is non-singular.

Proof. If A is nonsingular, then the equations $As_i = e_i$, $i = 1, \ldots, n$, can all be solved, so A has an inverse. If A has an inverse, then $Ax = b$ has a solution for *any* b (namely, $x = A^{-1}b$), so no row of A can be a linear combination of the others, and therefore A is nonsingular.

The following is an example of matrix inversion.

Example showing how to invert a matrix

Given the matrix

$$A = \begin{pmatrix} 1 & 2 & 2 \\ 3 & 2 & 1 \\ 2 & 3 & 2 \end{pmatrix},$$

find A^{-1}.

The procedure is shown in Table 1–6. As in Table 1–2, the first three columns in Tableau 0 give A. The next three columns give e_1, e_2, and e_3, that is, the right-hand side of the equations $As_1 = e_1$, $As_2 = e_2$, and $As_3 = e_3$, respectively. We then proceed just as before to obtain a 1 in each of the first three columns of Tableau 3, except that now the rows are two elements longer than before. The sum column is again used as a check.

Table 1–6

MATRIX INVERSION

		a_1	a_2	a_3	e_1	e_2	e_3	Sum
	(0.1)	1	2	2	1	0	0	6
Tableau 0	(0.2)	3	2	1	0	1	0	7
	(0.3)	2	3	2	0	0	1	8
	(1.1)	1	2	2	1	0	0	6
Tableau 1	(1.2)	0	-4	-5	-3	1	0	-11
	(1.3)	0	-1	-2	-2	0	1	-4
	(2.1)	1	0	$-\frac{2}{4}$	$-\frac{2}{4}$	$\frac{2}{4}$	0	$\frac{2}{4}$
Tableau 2	(2.2)	0	1	$\frac{5}{4}$	$\frac{3}{4}$	$-\frac{1}{4}$	0	$\frac{11}{4}$
	(2.3)	0	0	$-\frac{3}{4}$	$-\frac{5}{4}$	$-\frac{1}{4}$	1	$-\frac{5}{4}$
	(3.1)	1	0	0	$\frac{1}{3}$	$\frac{2}{3}$	$-\frac{2}{3}$	$\frac{4}{3}$
Tableau 3	(3.2)	0	1	0	$-\frac{4}{3}$	$-\frac{2}{3}$	$\frac{5}{3}$	$\frac{2}{3}$
	(3.3)	0	0	1	$\frac{5}{3}$	$\frac{1}{3}$	$-\frac{4}{3}$	$\frac{5}{3}$

From Tableau 3 we read the answer:

$$s_1 = \begin{pmatrix} \frac{1}{3} \\ -\frac{4}{3} \\ \frac{5}{3} \end{pmatrix}, \qquad s_2 = \begin{pmatrix} \frac{2}{3} \\ -\frac{2}{3} \\ \frac{1}{3} \end{pmatrix}, \qquad s_3 = \begin{pmatrix} -\frac{2}{3} \\ \frac{5}{3} \\ -\frac{4}{3} \end{pmatrix},$$

or

$$A^{-1} = \begin{pmatrix} \frac{1}{3} & \frac{2}{3} & -\frac{2}{3} \\ -\frac{4}{3} & -\frac{2}{3} & \frac{5}{3} \\ \frac{5}{3} & \frac{1}{3} & -\frac{4}{3} \end{pmatrix}.$$

From Table 1–6 it can be seen that in the inversion of an n-by-n matrix, n of the first $2n$ columns are always $e_1, e_2, \ldots, e_n$. In hand computing, where storage space for these e columns is cheap, i.e., paper is plentiful, there is no occasion to take advantage of this fact. In machine computing, where storage space is frequently in short supply, it is advantageous to store the fourth column of Tableau 1 where the first column of Tableau 0 was stored. Likewise, the fourth and fifth columns of Tableau 2 may be stored where the first and second columns of the original matrix were, and so on.

The appearance of the expression $A(Sb)$ in Eq. (1–5.2) above raises the question: Can we define the product of two matrices, A and B, in such a fashion that

$$A(Bx) = (AB)x \qquad (1\text{–}5.4)$$

for *any* vector x? Such a definition would be convenient, for we could then drop many parentheses. If this equation is to hold for any x, it must certainly hold for $x = e_1$. But

$$A(Be_1) = AB_1,$$

where B_1 denotes the first column of (AB), and

$$(AB)e_1 = (AB)_1,$$

where $(AB)_1$ denotes the first column of (AB). That is, the first column of (AB) must be defined to be $A(B_1)$: $(AB)_1 = A(B_1)$. Likewise, using e_i, we find that we must define

$$(AB)_i = A(B_i) \qquad \text{for} \quad i = 1, \ldots, n,$$

where n is the number of columns of B. In words, the ith column of the product AB is A times the ith column of B. Will this definition cause Eq. (1–5.4) to be satisfied for any arbitrary vector x? Yes, it will, for on writing

$$x = x_1e_1 + \cdots + x_ne_n,$$

and using the definition of AB just given, we obtain

$$A(Bx) = A(B_1x_1) + \cdots + A(B_nx_n) = x_1(AB_1) + \cdots + x_n(AB_n)$$
$$= x_1(AB)_1 + \cdots + x_n(AB)_n = (AB)x.$$

With this definition of AB, therefore, $A(Bx) = (AB)x$ for all x.

Mechanically, there is nothing new in matrix multiplication. Think of the columns of B as so many column vectors; multiply each of them by A, and write the resulting vectors side by side.

Examples

$$\begin{pmatrix} 2 & 3 & 1 \\ -1 & 2 & 1 \\ 7 & -5 & 8 \end{pmatrix} \begin{pmatrix} 2 & 1 \\ 3 & 4 \\ -1 & 1 \end{pmatrix} = \begin{pmatrix} 12 & 15 \\ 3 & 8 \\ -9 & -5 \end{pmatrix},$$

$$\begin{pmatrix} 3 & 2 & 5 & 4 \\ -6 & 4 & -2 & 1 \end{pmatrix} \begin{pmatrix} 3 & 1 & 4 \\ 2 & 3 & 5 \\ 1 & 5 & -2 \\ 2 & 4 & 1 \end{pmatrix} = \begin{pmatrix} 26 & 50 & 16 \\ -10 & 0 & 1 \end{pmatrix}.$$

Equation (1–5.4) has a very simple interpretation in terms of transformation. The term $A(Bx)$ says transform x by B, then transform the result by A. But since $A(Bx) = (AB)x$, the result is the same as performing the single transform (AB) on x. That is, (AB) represents the composite transformation resulting from transformation first by B, then by A.

Note that for AB to be defined, it is not necessary that A and B be square, but only that A have the same number of columns as B has rows.

From the above discussion, it follows that if A is nonsingular, $AA^{-1} = I$, where I denotes a matrix with 1's in all the diagonal positions and 0's everywhere else. Observe that $AI = IA = A$; therefore I is called the identity matrix. (The letter E is also used sometimes to denote the identity.)

Matrix multiplication is associative, that is $A(BC) = (AB)C$. To show this fact, we again use the Σ notation, familiar from Section 1–2. Since the *order* in which a set of numbers is summed does not affect the final total,

$$\sum_{i=1}^{m}\left(\sum_{j=1}^{n} a_{ij}\right) = \sum_{j=1}^{n}\left(\sum_{i=1}^{m} a_{ij}\right).$$

Now let A have m columns and B, n columns. Then, the k, l position of $(AB)C$ is

$$[(AB)C]_{kl} = \sum_{i=1}^{n}\left(\sum_{j=1}^{m} a_{kj}b_{ji}\right)c_{il} = \sum_{i=1}^{n}\left(\sum_{j=1}^{m} a_{kj}b_{ji}c_{il}\right),$$

while the same position of $A(BC)$ is

$$[A(BC)]_{kl} = \sum_{j=1}^{m} a_{kj}\left(\sum_{i=1}^{n} b_{ji}c_{il}\right) = \sum_{j=1}^{m}\left(\sum_{i=1}^{n} a_{kj}b_{ji}c_{il}\right)$$

$$= \sum_{i=1}^{n}\left(\sum_{j=1}^{m} a_{kj}b_{ji}c_{il}\right) = [(AB)C]_{kl}.$$

Therefore, $(AB)C = A(BC)$. The reader should verify the rule that

$$A(B + C) = AB + AC.$$

So far, the properties of matrix multiplication are very similar to those of ordinary multiplication. But an important difference must be emphasized. With matrices, it is *not* generally true that $AB = BA$, as the reader will see by taking almost any pair of matrices at random. (See Problem 1.) There is, however, one important case in which $BA = AB$, namely when $B = A^{-1}$, for we know that $AA^{-1} = I$, and we can prove

Theorem 1–8. $A^{-1}A = I$.

Proof. $A^{-1} = S$ is nonsingular, for if it were singular, then there would exist a vector $x \neq 0$ such that $A^{-1}x = 0$. Multiplying both sides of this equation by A gives $AA^{-1}x = 0$ or $x = 0$, contrary to assumption. Therefore A^{-1} is nonsingular and $(A^{-1})^{-1}$ exists. Then

$$
\begin{aligned}
(A^{-1}A) &= (A^{-1}A)\big(A^{-1}(A^{-1})^{-1}\big) && \text{because } A^{-1}(A^{-1})^{-1} = I \\
&= A^{-1}(AA^{-1})(A^{-1})^{-1} && \text{because matrix multiplication} \\
& && \text{is associative} \\
&= A^{-1}(A^{-1})^{-1} && \text{because } AA^{-1} = I \\
&= I. && \text{Q.E.D.}
\end{aligned}
$$

Note that the theorem shows that $(A^{-1})^{-1} = A$.

PROBLEMS

1. Find the products AB, BA, $(AB)c$, and $A(Bc)$, where

$$
A = \begin{pmatrix} 2 & 1 \\ 1 & 3 \end{pmatrix}, \qquad B = \begin{pmatrix} -1 & 3 \\ 5 & 2 \end{pmatrix}, \qquad c = \begin{pmatrix} 1 \\ 1 \end{pmatrix}.
$$

2. Using A of Problem 1, find A^{-1}. Verify that $A^{-1}A = AA^{-1} = I$.

3. Find the inverse of the input-output matrix in Eq. (1–2.4). Explain why s_{ij}, the ij element of this inverse, may be called "the total output of industry i required, directly and indirectly, to provide one unit of final consumption of industry j's output."

4. The final demand vector, F, shown in Eq. (1–1.2) is composed of personal consumption, C, plus investment, V, plus government, G, as follows:

$$
\begin{array}{ccccccc}
C & + & V & + & G & = & F
\end{array}
$$
$$
\begin{pmatrix} 15 \\ 20 \\ 10 \end{pmatrix} + \begin{pmatrix} 2 \\ 20 \\ 3 \end{pmatrix} + \begin{pmatrix} 3 \\ 8 \\ 1 \end{pmatrix} = \begin{pmatrix} 20 \\ 48 \\ 14 \end{pmatrix}.
$$

Referring to the matrix consisting of columns C, V, and G as B, find $A^{-1}B$, where A^{-1} is the inverse found in Problem 3. Why can the element in the lower right-hand corner of the resulting matrix be called "the agricultural output going, directly or indirectly, to government's final demand"? Why is the sum of all the elements in the ith row of $A^{-1}B$ equal to x_i found in Problem 2, Section 1-3?

5. Let the row matrix (or vector) $L = (0.2 \quad 0.1 \quad 0.15)$ show the labor coefficients —thousand man-years per billions dollars of output—for the three industries of the preceding problems. Find the total employment $= LA^{-1}F$. Find the portion of $LA^{-1}F$ due to personal consumption $(LA^{-1}C)$, that due to investment, and that due to government consumption. Why will the sum of these three components be the total employment previously found?

6. Show that if A and B are n-by-n nonsingular matrices, then $(AB)^{-1} = B^{-1}A^{-1}$.

7. What is the effect on A^{-1} of
   a) interchanging two rows of A?
   b) multiplying one row of A by a constant?
   c) multiplying one column of A by a constant?

8. Show that the rank of AB does not exceed the rank of either A or B.

1-6 PARTITIONED MATRICES AND VECTORS

We shall frequently find it convenient to think of a vector of vectors, that is, of a single vector partitioned into two or more subvectors. Thus

$$a = (a_1, a_2),$$

where a is a row vector and a_1 is the vector consisting of first p elements of a, while a_2 is the vector consisting of the remaining $n - p$ elements of a. The product of two partitioned vectors can be written in terms of the subvectors in an expression formally identical to the rule for multiplication in terms of single numbers. Thus, if

$$a = (a_1, a_2) \qquad \text{and} \qquad b = \begin{pmatrix} b_1 \\ b_2 \end{pmatrix},$$

where a_1 and a_2 have the same number of columns as b_1 and b_2, respectively, have rows, then

$$ab = (a_1, a_2)\begin{pmatrix} b_1 \\ b_2 \end{pmatrix} = a_1 b_1 + a_2 b_2. \tag{1-6.1}$$

The verification of this formula follows immediately from the definition of the multiplication of vectors.

This result extends also to matrices. Suppose, for example, that we have two matrices, A and B, partitioned into submatrices as follows:

$$A = \begin{pmatrix} A_{11} & A_{12} \\ \hline A_{21} & A_{22} \end{pmatrix}, \qquad B = \begin{pmatrix} B_{11} & B_{12} \\ \hline B_{21} & B_{22} \end{pmatrix}, \tag{1-6.2}$$

where

$$\left.\begin{matrix}A_{11} \text{ and } A_{21}\\ A_{12} \text{ and } A_{22}\end{matrix}\right\} \begin{matrix}\text{have the same number}\\ \text{of columns as}\end{matrix} \left.\begin{matrix}B_{11} \text{ and } B_{12}\\ B_{21} \text{ and } B_{22}\end{matrix}\right\} \text{have rows.}$$

Then application of Eq. (1–6.1) to the elements of the product AB shows that

$$AB = \begin{pmatrix} A_{11}B_{11} + A_{12}B_{21} & A_{11}B_{12} + A_{12}B_{22} \\ A_{21}B_{11} + A_{22}B_{21} & A_{21}B_{12} + A_{22}B_{22} \end{pmatrix}. \qquad (1\text{–}6.3)$$

A partitioned matrix may also be inverted in terms of its submatrices. For inversion, it is necessary that the diagonal submatrices, A_{11}, A_{22}, etc., be square. Then we may write Tableau 0 of Table 1–6 as

$$\begin{pmatrix} A_{11} & A_{12} & I & 0 \\ A_{21} & A_{22} & 0 & I \end{pmatrix}. \qquad (1\text{–}6.4)$$

Now the rows of the product of two matrices, AB, are linear combinations of the rows of the *second* matrix. Therefore we may premultiply the first row (of submatrices) of (1–6.4) by A_{11}^{-1} to obtain the equivalent system

$$\begin{pmatrix} I & A_{11}^{-1}A_{12} & A_{11}^{-1} & 0 \\ A_{21} & A_{22} & 0 & I \end{pmatrix}. \qquad (1\text{–}6.5)$$

Any vector, s_i, which was a solution of one of the systems of equations represented by (1–6.4) would continue to be a solution of the corresponding system in (1–6.5). The step from (1–6.4) to (1–6.5) corresponds to dividing the pivot row by the pivot element in the one-row-at-a-time Gauss-Jordan process.

Next, just as in the Gauss-Jordan process, we multiply the first row of (1–6.5) by A_{21} and subtract the result from the second row to obtain the equivalent system

$$\begin{pmatrix} I & A_{11}^{-1}A_{12} & A_{11}^{-1} & 0 \\ 0 & A_{22} - A_{21}A_{11}^{-1}A_{12} & -A_{21}A_{11}^{-1} & I \end{pmatrix}. \qquad (1\text{–}6.6)$$

Continuing the reduction process, we finally obtain

$$\begin{pmatrix} I & 0 & A_{11}^{-1} + A_{11}^{-1}A_{12}Q^{-1}A_{21}A_{11}^{-1} & -A_{11}^{-1}A_{12}Q^{-1} \\ 0 & I & -Q^{-1}A_{21}A_{11}^{-1} & Q^{-1} \end{pmatrix},$$

$$(1\text{–}6.7)$$

where $Q = A_{22} - A_{21}A_{11}^{-1}A_{12}$. The right-hand matrix in (1–6.7) is the formula for A^{-1} which we were seeking.

In subsequent sections, we shall see various theoretical applications of this formula. It is also useful in the inversion by electronic computers of matrices which are too big to fit into the internal memory of the machine all at once. It is also valuable in finding the inverses of a number of matrices which all have the same A_{11}. If A_{11} is large in relation to A_{22}, and A_{11}^{-1} is known, A^{-1} can be calculated from (1–6.7) with less labor than if we started from the beginning by the usual method.

1-7 CHANGING THE INVERSE WHEN
ONE COLUMN OF A MATRIX IS CHANGED

The method developed in this section plays a central role in linear programming, which is to be discussed in Chapter 4, and, therefore, should be thoroughly understood. In its own right, the method has often proved useful in input-output analysis when revisions in a matrix have been found necessary after the matrix was inverted.

Suppose that an inverse of a large n-by-n matrix A has been computed and that it is now desired to find the inverse of a new matrix, A^1, which differs from A only in that A_r, the rth column of A, has been replaced by a new column, A_k, where $k > n$. We assume that A^1 is nonsingular. Define $S = A^{-1}$ and $p = SA_k = A^{-1}A_k$. The matrix equations $AS = I$ and $Ap = A_k$ may also be written as

$$p_1 A_1 + \cdots + p_r A_r + \cdots + p_n A_n = A_k, \qquad (1\text{–}7.1)$$

$$s_{1i} A_1 + \cdots + s_{ri} A_r + \cdots + s_{ni} A_n = e_i, \qquad i = 1, \ldots, n. \qquad (1\text{–}7.2)$$

By solving (1–7.1) for A_r, we have

$$A_r = -\frac{p_1}{p_r} A_1 + \cdots - \frac{p_{r-1}}{p_r} A_{r-1} + \frac{1}{p_r} A_k$$
$$-\frac{p_{r+1}}{p_r} A_{r+1} + \cdots - \frac{p_n}{p_r} A_n, \qquad (1\text{–}7.3)$$

where we have inserted A_k between A_{r-1} and A_{r+1} in the order of the vectors. That $p_r \neq 0$ follows from the assumption that A^1 is nonsingular. Now by substituting (1–7.3) into (1–7.2) and collecting terms, we obtain

$$\left(s_{1i} - \frac{s_{ri} p_1}{p_r}\right) A_1 + \cdots + \left(s_{r-1,i} - \frac{s_{ri} p_{r-1}}{p_r}\right) A_{r-1} + \left(\frac{s_{ri}}{p_r}\right) A_k$$
$$+ \cdots + \left(s_{r+1,i} - \frac{s_{ri} p_{r+1}}{p_r}\right) A_{r+1}$$
$$+ \cdots + \left(s_{ni} - \frac{s_{ri} p_n}{p_r}\right) A_n = e_i \qquad \text{for} \quad i = 1, \ldots, n.$$
$$(1\text{–}7.4)$$

The coefficients of the equation for e_i are, by the definition of the inverse, the ith column of the inverse. Therefore, $(A^1)^{-1}$ is given by

$$(A^1)^{-1} = \begin{pmatrix} s_{11} - s_{r1}p_1/p_r & \cdots & s_{1n} - s_{rn}p_1/p_r \\ s_{r-1,1} - s_{r1}p_{r-1}/p_r & \cdots & s_{r-1,n} - s_{rn}p_{r-1}/p_r \\ s_{r1}/p_r & \cdots & s_{rn}/p_r \\ \vdots & & \vdots \\ s_{r+1,1} - s_{r1}p_{r+1}/p_r & \cdots & s_{r+1,n} - s_{rn}p_{r+1}/p_r \\ s_{n,1} - s_{r1}p_n/p_r & \cdots & s_{nn} - s_{rn}p_n/p_r \end{pmatrix}.$$

By letting S^r denote the rth row of S, we can compactly write this equation as

$$(A^1)^{-1} = S - \frac{1}{p_r}pS^r + \frac{1}{p_r}e_rS^r. \tag{1-7.5}$$

We can easily remember the result in Eq. (1–7.5) by noting that it is just the result of a pivot operation. Mechanically, we write p at the left of $S = A^{-1}$ as follows:

$$\begin{matrix} p_1 & s_{11} & \cdots & s_{1n} \\ \vdots & \vdots & & \vdots \\ p_r & s_{r1} & \cdots & s_{rn} \\ \vdots & \vdots & & \vdots \\ p_n & s_{n1} & \cdots & s_{nn} \end{matrix}$$

and then we pivot on p_r to get

$$\begin{matrix} 0 & s_{11} - s_{r1}p_1/p_r & \cdots & s_{1n} - s_{1n}p_1/p_r \\ \vdots & \vdots & & \vdots \\ 1 & s_{r1}/p_r & \cdots & s_{rn}/p_r \\ \vdots & \vdots & & \vdots \\ 0 & s_{n1} - s_{r1}p_n/p_r & \cdots & s_{nn} - s_{rn}p_n/p_r \end{matrix}$$

The n columns on the right are the right-hand side of Eq. (1–7.5). If we also have the solution, x, of $Ax = b$ and want to find the solution of $A^1y = b$, we can apply Eq. (1–7.5) to find that

$$y = (A^1)^{-1}b = \left[S - \frac{1}{p_r}pS^r + \frac{1}{p_r}e_rS^r\right]b = x - \frac{x_r}{p_r}p + \frac{x_r}{p_r}e_r. \tag{1-7.6}$$

Inspection shows that the right-hand side of Eq. (1–7.6) can also be remembered as the result of writing x and p side by side and pivoting on p_r. We shall therefore call Eqs. (1–7.5) and (1–7.6) the *pivot rules* for the transformation of a matrix inverse or solution of a system of equations when one column of the matrix is changed.

Table 1–7

CHANGING A COLUMN

	p	s_1	s_2	s_3	A_k
(0.1)	$\frac{2}{3}$	$\frac{1}{3}$	$\frac{2}{3}$	$-\frac{2}{3}$	2
(0.2)	$\frac{1}{3}$	$-\frac{4}{3}$	$-\frac{2}{3}$	$\frac{5}{3}$	3
(0.3)	$\frac{1}{3}$	$\frac{5}{3}$	$\frac{1}{3}$	$-\frac{4}{3}$	3
(1.1)	0	3	2	-4	
(1.2)	1	-4	-2	5	
(1.3)	0	3	2	-3	

Example. Find the inverse of the matrix obtained by replacing A_2 of the matrix A in the example of Section 1–5 by

$$A_k = \begin{pmatrix} 2 \\ 3 \\ 3 \end{pmatrix}.$$

That is, find the inverse of

$$A^1 = \begin{pmatrix} 1 & 2 & 2 \\ 3 & 3 & 1 \\ 2 & 3 & 2 \end{pmatrix}.$$

In Table 1–7, the value of A^{-1} found in Table 1–6 is shown in the column headed s_1, s_2, s_3. Write A_k in the right-hand column of the table. Then compute $p = A^{-1}A_k$, and write p in the first column of the table. Now proceed just as if we were on the rth step in the inversion of a matrix. By elementary row operation, obtain e_r in the p-column. Then $(A^1)^{-1}$ will appear in the S-columns.

PROBLEMS

1. Find the inverse of

$$A = \begin{pmatrix} 2 & 2 & 2 \\ 3 & 3 & 1 \\ 2 & 3 & 2 \end{pmatrix}.$$

Note that A differs from A^1 of the text only in the first column.

2. Letting A' denote the transpose of A, show that $(A')^{-1} = (A^{-1})'$. How can this fact be used to apply the above method to finding, from A^{-1}, the new inverse, when one *row* of A is changed?

*1–8 ITERATIVE METHODS

Is it always necessary to go through the whole Gauss-Jordan process to solve a set of equations? Can we ever get *close* to the solution with far less work? Yes, fortunately, for some types of matrices, we can. And, even more fortunately, input-output matrices are all of a type for which such *approximate* solutions can be found quickly. The calculation procedure is very simple: Write the input-output equations in the form

$$x - Ax = b, \tag{1–8.1}$$

where A is the matrix of α's of Section 1–1. Then set

$$
\begin{aligned}
x^{(0)} &= b, \\
x^{(1)} &= Ax^{(0)} + b, \\
x^{(2)} &= Ax^{(1)} + b, \\
&\vdots \\
x^{(n)} &= Ax^{(n-1)} + b,
\end{aligned}
\tag{1–8.2}
$$

where $x^{(n)}$ is the nth approximation to the solution of Eq. (1–8.1).

In economic terms, first set the output equal to only final demands. Then increase it to allow for the intermediate goods needed by the first approximation; increase again to allow for the intermediates needed by the second approximation, and so on.

Clearly, if n is large, say 50, and $x^{(3)}$ or $x^{(4)}$ is so close to the true solution, x^*, that we are satisfied with it, we have saved ourselves a lot of work.

"But what," I hope I hear the reader asking, "do you mean by two vectors being 'close' together, and how on earth can you tell how far $x^{(4)}$ is from x^* if you don't know what x^* is?" The answer to the first question lies in the concept of the *norm* of a vector; the answer to the second requires, in addition, the norm of a matrix. After introducing these concepts, we will derive bounds for the difference between $x^{(n)}$ and x^*.

Norms of Vectors

We can say how far apart two vectors are if we can say how "long" a vector is, that is, how long the line is which connects the point 0 with the point x. For if $\|x\|$ represents the length of any vector, then the length of the vector of the difference of a and b, $\|a - b\|$, serves as a measure of how close together they are. How shall we measure the length of a vector? In two dimensions, the usual length of the vector (x_1, x_2) is $\sqrt{x_1^2 + x_2^2}$. This rule readily generalizes to n dimensions:

$$\|x\| = \sqrt{x'x}. \tag{1–8.3}$$

This formula, called the Euclidean length (or norm), gives *one* perfectly good way of measuring length.   Using it we might, for example, say that the method of least squares minimizes the *distance between* the actual and predicted vectors.   But why do we bother to take the square root?   Why not say $\|x\| = x'x$?   Because we certainly want *any* way of calculating a length of x to be such that multiplying each element of x by a scalar, λ, multiplies $\|x\|$ by λ:

   a) $\|\lambda x\| = |\lambda| \cdot \|x\|$.

Other properties which *any* rule for calculating a $\|x\|$ should certainly have are

   b) $\|0\| = 0$ and $\|x\| > 0$ if $x \neq 0$ (vector), and

   c) $\|x + y\| \leq \|x\| + \|y\|$.

   Property (c) comes from the requirement that the shortest distance between any two points must be a straight line.   Let us denote the points by x and $-y$.   Then we must have

$$\|x - (-y)\| \leq \|x\| + \|-y\|,$$

since $\|x\|$ is the distance from x to 0 and $\|-y\|$ is the distance to $-y$ from 0, while $\|x - (-y)\|$ is the distance directly from x to $-y$.   Since, by (a), $\|-y\| = \|y\|$, this requirement may therefore be written more simply as

   c) $\|x + y\| \leq \|x\| + \|y\|$.

   Any way of assigning a number, $\|x\|$, to each vector of a space in such a way that (a), (b), and (c) are satisfied is called a *norm* of the space.   Then $\|x\|$ is read "the norm of x."   Besides Eq. (1–8.3), known as the Euclidean norm, there are two more important examples:

$$\|x\| = \sum_{i=1}^{n} |x_i| \qquad \text{(the } l\text{-norm)}, \qquad\qquad (1\text{--}8.4)$$

$$\|x\| = \max_{i} |x_i| \qquad \text{(the } m\text{-norm)}. \qquad\qquad (1\text{--}8.5)$$

The reader can verify at a glance that these two norms have the three required properties.

Example

$$\|(1, -3, 2)\|_l = 6,$$
$$\|(1, -3, 2)\|_m = 3,$$
$$\|(1, -3, 2)\|_E = \sqrt{14} = 3.74,$$

where the l, m, and E [for Euclidean, the norm of Eq. (1–8.3)] show which norm is used. (The l refers to Lebesgue, a mathematician of the early years of this century.) With each of these norms, it is easily seen that if $x^{(k)}$ is any sequence of vectors and x^* is a vector such that

$$\lim_{k \to \infty} \|x^{(k)} - x^*\| = 0,$$

then

$$\lim_{k \to \infty} x^{(k)} = x^*.$$

That is, convergence in norm implies element-by-element convergence of the sequence of vectors.

Norms of Matrices

We come back now to the $x^{(k)}$-sequence defined by Eq. (1–8.2), where

$$x^{(k+1)} = Ax^{(k)} + b \qquad \text{and} \qquad x^* = Ax^* + b.$$

Subtracting the second equation from the first, we obtain

$$x^{(k+1)} - x^* = A(x^{(k)} - x^*). \tag{1–8.6}$$

If we know $\|x^{(k)} - x^*\|$, can we put an upper limit on $\|x^{(k+1)} - x^*\|$? Is there a number, call it $\|A\|$, such that

$$\|x^{(k+1)} - x^*\| \le \|A\| \cdot \|x^{(k)} - x^*\|?$$

This question leads us to *define the norm of the matrix A, $\|A\|$, as the smallest number such that*

$$\|Ax\| \le \|A\| \cdot \|x\| \qquad \text{for all} \quad x. \tag{1–8.7}$$

Intuitively, $\|A\|$ is the greatest "stretch" which multiplication by A performs on any vector. Applying this definition to Eq. (1–8.6), we get

$$\|x^{(k+p)} - x^*\| \le \|A\|^p \cdot \|x^{(k)} - x^*\|, \qquad p = 1, 2, \ldots, j, \tag{1–8.8}$$

and, if $\|A\| < 1$, we see that

$$\|x^{(n)} - x^*\| \to 0 \qquad \text{and} \qquad x^{(n)} \to x^* \quad \text{as} \quad n \to \infty.$$

Luckily, $\|A\|$ can be readily calculated for the m- and l-vector norms, namely

$$\|A\|_m = \max_i \sum_{j=1}^{n} |a_{ij}|, \tag{1–8.9}$$

$$\|A\|_l = \max_j \sum_{i=1}^{n} |a_{ij}|, \qquad \text{where A is n by n.} \tag{1–8.10}$$

That is, the *l*-norm is the maximum column sum of absolute values, while $\|A\|_m$ is the maximum row sum of absolute values.

We shall prove the equation for $\|A\|_l$ and leave that for $\|A\|_m$ as an exercise.

Let $\alpha = \max_j \sum_{i=1}^{n} |a_{ij}|$. Then

$$\|A\|_l \leq \alpha, \qquad (1\text{-}8.11)$$

for

$$\|Ax\|_l = \sum_{i=1}^{n} \left| \sum_{j=1}^{n} a_{ij}x_j \right| \leq \sum_i \sum_j |a_{ij}| \cdot |x_j|$$
$$= \sum_j |x_j| \sum_i |a_{ij}| \leq \sum_j |x_j|\alpha = \alpha \|x\|_l.$$

On the other hand, let k be the number of the column with the largest sum of absolute values, so that

$$\alpha = \sum_{i=1}^{n} |a_{ik}|,$$

and then choose a vector x with $x_k = 1$ and $x_j = 0$ for $j \neq k$. Then $\|x\| = 1$, and

$$\|Ax\| = \sum_i \left| \sum_j a_{ij}x_j \right| = \sum_i |a_{ik}| = \alpha = \alpha \|x\|.$$

Hence

$$\|A\|_l \geq \alpha. \qquad (1\text{-}8.12)$$

Combining Eqs. (1-8.11) and (1-8.12), we get $\|A\|_l = \alpha$.

When A is the matrix of an open input-output system, its elements are all positive (or zero), and its column sums are all less than one, since each industry has a labor and capital input. Therefore, $\|A\|_l < 1$, and according to Eq. (1-8.8), the solution process described by Eq. (1-8.2) is convergent.

Error Bounds for the Iterative Process

To find an upper bound for the error, $\|x^{(k)} - x^*\|$, at any stage of the calculation, note first that for any positive integer p,

$$x^{(k+p)} - x^{(k)} = x^{(k+1)} - x^{(k)} + x^{(k+2)} - x^{(k+1)}$$
$$+ x^{(k+3)} - x^{(k+2)} + \cdots + x^{(k+p)} - x^{(k+p-1)}.$$

So, by Property (c) of norms, we have

$$\|x^{(k+p)} - x^{(k)}\| \leq \|x^{(k+1)} - x^{(k)}\| + \|x^{(k+2)} - x^{(k+1)}\|$$
$$+ \cdots + \|x^{(k+p)} - x^{(k+p-1)}\|. \qquad (1\text{-}8.13)$$

But since

$$x^{(m+1)} = Ax^m + b \qquad \text{and} \qquad x^{(m)} = Ax^{m-1} + b,$$

subtraction gives

$$x^{(m+1)} - x^{(m)} = A(x^{(m)} - x^{(m-1)}) \qquad \text{for all} \quad m > k \geq 1.$$

Repeatedly applying this equation, we obtain

$$\begin{aligned}
\|x^{(m+1)} - x^{(m)}\| &\leq \|A\| \cdot \|x^{(m)} - x^{(m-1)}\| \\
&\leq \|A\|^2 \cdot \|x^{(m-1)} - x^{(m-2)}\| \\
&\leq \|A\|^{m-k} \cdot \|x^{(k+1)} - x^{(k)}\|.
\end{aligned} \qquad (1\text{-}8.14)$$

By applying the first of these inequalities to the second term on the right-hand side of (1–8.13), the second to the third term, and so on, we obtain

$$\|x^{(k+p)} - x^{(k)}\| \leq (1 + \|A\| + \|A\|^2 + \cdots + \|A\|^{p-1})\|x^{(k+1)} - x^{(k)}\|. \qquad (1\text{-}8.15)$$

If $\|A\| < 1$, we know that as $p \to \infty$,

$$x^{(k+p)} \to x^*, \qquad \text{and} \qquad (1 + \|A\| + \|A\|^2 + \cdots),$$

being a geometric series, goes to $1/(1 - \|A\|)$. Therefore, in the limit, Eq. (1–8.15) becomes

$$\|x^* - x^{(k)}\| \leq \frac{\|x^{(k+1)} - x^{(k)}\|}{1 - \|A\|}.$$

Applying Eq. (1–8.14) once again, we get the more useful form

$$\|x^* - x^{(k)}\| \leq \frac{\|A\| \cdot \|x^{(k)} - x^{(k-1)}\|}{1 - \|A\|} \qquad \text{for} \quad k \geq 2. \qquad (1\text{-}8.16)$$

Note that Eq. (1–8.16) enables one to be sure that he is close to the answer without knowing the answer!

In actual input-output practice, the Gauss-Jordan method is used when the complete inverse is desired, and a slight modification of the above iterative procedure is employed when only the solution for one particular b is needed. Using this modified iterative procedure, known as the *Seidel method*, one starts with $x^{(1)} = b_i$ and successively calculates $x^{(2)}$, $x^{(3)}$, etc., by

$$x_i^{(k+1)} = \left(\sum_{j=1}^{i-1} a_{ij} x_j^{(k+1)} + \sum_{j=1}^{n} a_{ij} x_j^{(k)} + b_i \right).$$

In input-output matrices, the b_i and a_{ij} are all either positive or zero, so each element of x increases with each iteration: $x_i^{(k+1)} \geq x_i^{(k)}$. Moreover, starting from the same $x^{(k)}$, we find that $x^{(k+1)}$ calculated by the Seidel method is larger than $x^{(k+1)}$ calculated by the original iterative method. The Seidel method therefore approaches the solution more rapidly. Inequality (1–8.16) is satisfied with room to spare. Stronger inequalities are known.

PROBLEMS

1. Use the iterative method to solve the input-output system of Eq. (1–1.1). Go only to $x^{(3)}$. Obtain an upper limit for $\|x^{(3)} - x^*\|_l$.

2. Use the Seidel method on the same problem. Note that one can accelerate convergence by arranging the sectors so that the largest coefficients fall to the left of the diagonal. This "triangularization" of matrices is used often in input-output work.

3. Show that if $\|A\| < 1$, then

$$(I - A)^{-1} = I + A + A^2 + A^3 + \cdots$$

Observe the relation between this series and the process described by Eq. (1–8.2). Interpret the series economically.

4. Prove Eq. (1–8.9).

5. After reading Chapter 3, write a FORTRAN program to perform the following:
   a) Find $\|A\|$ of an N-by-N matrix A.
   b) Solve $x = Ax + b$ by the simple iterative method. Continue iterations until you are sure that your solution differs, in the l-norm, from the true solution by less than some specified amount, which you may call TOLER.
   c) Repeat part (b), using the Seidel method.

CHAPTER 2

THE METHOD OF LEAST SQUARES

2-1 LEAST-SQUARES COMPUTATIONS

A very common problem in statistics is to use observations of n "independent" variables $x_1, \ldots, x_n$ to explain a dependent variable, y. A relation of the sort

$$\hat{y} = b_1 x_1 + \cdots + b_n x_n \qquad (2\text{-}1.1)$$

is sought, where $\hat{y}$ is the "predicted" value of y, and the $b_1, \ldots, b_n$ are determined so as to minimize the sum of the squares of the deviations between y and $\hat{y}$ for a number, T, of observations. That is, if y_t denotes the tth observation of y, and x_{ti} denotes the tth observation of x_i, then the b's are determined so as to minimize

$$s = \sum_{t=1}^{T} \left(y_t - (b_1 x_{t1} + b_2 x_{t2} + \cdots + b_n x_{tn}) \right)^2.$$

We can accomplish this minimization by setting the derivative of s with respect to each of the b's equal to zero. Thus we find that the b's must satisfy the following linear equations:

$$\frac{\partial s}{\partial b_1} = 2 \left[\sum_{t=1}^{T} y_t x_{t1} - \left(b_1 \sum_{t=1}^{T} x_{t1}^2 + b_2 \sum_{t=1}^{T} x_{t1} x_{t2} + \cdots + b_n \sum_{t=1}^{T} x_{t1} x_{tn} \right) \right] = 0,$$

$$\vdots$$

$$\frac{\partial s}{\partial b_n} = 2 \left[\sum_{t=1}^{T} y_t x_{tn} - \left(b_1 \sum_{t=1}^{T} x_{t1} x_{tn} + b_2 \sum_{t=1}^{T} x_{t2} x_{tn} + \cdots + b_n \sum_{t=1}^{T} x_{tn}^2 \right) \right] = 0.$$

$$(2\text{-}1.2)$$

To use matrix notation most effectively in writing these equations, we need the concept of the *transpose* of a matrix. A matrix B is said to be the transpose of a matrix A if $a_{ij} = b_{ji}$. We shall use the notation A' to denote the transpose of A; the notation A^T is also often used. For example,

$$\text{if} \quad A = \begin{pmatrix} 2 & 5 \\ 4 & 3 \\ 1 & 7 \end{pmatrix}, \quad \text{then} \quad A' = \begin{pmatrix} 2 & 4 & 1 \\ 5 & 3 & 7 \end{pmatrix}.$$

It is left as an exercise for the student to show that $(AB)' = B'A'$.

Upon returning to Eq. (2–1.2) and defining

$$y = \begin{pmatrix} y_1 \\ \vdots \\ y_T \end{pmatrix}, \quad X = \begin{pmatrix} x_{11} & \cdots & x_{1n} \\ \vdots & & \vdots \\ x_{T1} & \cdots & x_{Tn} \end{pmatrix}, \quad \text{and} \quad b = \begin{pmatrix} b_1 \\ \vdots \\ b_n \end{pmatrix},$$

we can write Eq. (2–1.2) in matrix form (after canceling the 2's) as

$$X'Xb = X'y. \qquad (2\text{–}1.3)$$

(It may take a moment's thought to see why Eqs. (2–1.2) and (2–1.3) are the same, but the thought is good practice in the definition of matrix multiplication.) Here $X'X$ is known as the cross product matrix. These n equations in n unknowns can be solved by the methods already developed. The resulting b, $b = (X'X)^{-1}X'y$, is called the vector of *regression coefficients* of y on $x_1, \ldots, x_n$.

The matrix $X'X$ has an important feature which reduces the labor of computing it. Namely, it is *symmetric*, for a matrix A is said to be symmetric if $a_{ij} = a_{ji}$ for all i and j. In terms of the transpose, A is symmetric if $A' = A$. Since $(X'X)' = X'X$, by Problem 3, $X'X$ is symmetric. Only the elements on and above the diagonal need be calculated; the others can be filled in from the symmetry. Moreover, the inverse of a symmetric matrix is also symmetric, for if $A = A'$, then

$$I = (AA^{-1})' = (A^{-1})'A' = (A^{-1})'A,$$

and postmultiplying both sides of this equation by A^{-1} gives

$$A^{-1} = (A^{-1})'.$$

When working by hand, we can use this symmetry to lighten the load of calculations.

Example. A county agent observes that five farmers in his area have rather different yields on a certain crop, as shown in the y-column of Table 2–1. He suspects that most of the variability of the yield, y, may be due to the

Table 2-1

DATA

	X-matrix			y-column	Deviation from mean			
	X_1	X_2	X_3		$X - \bar{X}$			$y - \bar{y}$
Farm 1	1	10	5	17	0	5	0	2
Farm 2	1	5	1	10	0	0	−4	−5
Farm 3	1	0	6	12	0	−5	1	−3
Farm 4	1	10	3	16	0	5	−2	1
Farm 5	1	0	10	20	0	−5	5	5

Table 2-2

REGRESSION COMPUTATION

	$X'X$ $y'X$			$X'y$ $y'y$			
Tableau 1	5	25	25	75			
	25	225	85	380			
	25	85	171	415			
	75	380	415	1189			
Tableau 2	1	5	5	15			
	0	100	−40	5	100	−40	5
	0	−40	46	40	−40	46	40
	0	5	40	64	5	40	64
Tableau 3	1	0	7	14.75			
	0	1	−0.4	0.05			
	0	0	30	42			
	0	0	42	63.75			
Tableau 4	1	0	0	4.95			
	0	1	0	0.61			
	0	0	1	1.40			
	0	0	0	4.95			

varying amounts of phosphates, x_2, and nitrogen, x_3, used per acre, that is,

$$y = b_1 + b_2 x_2 + b_3 x_3, \quad \text{approximately.}$$

If we let $x_{t1} = 1$ for all values of t, this equation becomes

$$y = b_1 x_1 + b_2 x_2 + b_3 x_3,$$

and is of the form (2–1.1) above. The X-matrix observed by the county agent is shown in the first three columns of Table 2–1. We must find the b-vector.

The layout of computations shown in Tables 2–1 and 2–2 makes it possible for us to compute the regression coefficients, first of y on just x_1 and x_2, then of y on x_1, x_2, and x_3, and so on, adding one variable at a time.

To begin with, think of the four columns, X_1, X_2, X_3, and y as forming a single matrix (X, y). Then form

$$(X, y)'(X, y) = \begin{pmatrix} X' \\ y' \end{pmatrix} (X, y) = \begin{pmatrix} X'X & X'y \\ y'X & y'y \end{pmatrix}. \qquad (2\text{–}1.4)$$

The matrix on the right is shown in the first tableau of Table 2–2. Note that the coefficients of Eq. (2–1.3), $X'Xb = X'y$, are contained in the first three rows (in general, in the first n rows). The succeeding three tableaux show the familiar Gauss-Jordan process applied to solve these equations. The regression coefficients are $b = (4.95, 0.61, 1.40)$.

Note that if we had been regressing y on only x_1 and x_2, no elements of Tableau 1 would have been changed, except that the third row and column would not, of course, be present. Likewise, Tableau 2 and 3 would be unchanged, except for the deletion of the third row and column. The regression equation would be

$$\hat{y} = 14.75 + 0.05x_2,$$

and the sum of squared residuals would be 63.75. (We abbreviate $14.75x_1$ by 14.75, since $x_1 = 1$ always.) The third column, incidentally, gives the regression coefficient of x_3 on x_1 and x_2:

$$\hat{x}_3 = 7 - 0.4x_2,$$

with the sum of squares of residuals between $\hat{x}_{t3}$ and x_{t3} equal to 30.

The first row of Tableau 2 gives the regression coefficients of x_2, x_3, and y, each regressed (separately) on x_1:

$$\bar{x}_2 = 5, \qquad \bar{x}_3 = 5, \qquad \bar{y} = 15.$$

The regression coefficient of any variable on the constant variable, x_1, is, as the notation just used implies, simply the mean of the given variable. Why?

Sums of Squares and Cross Products of Residuals

For the further exploration of the contents of Table 2–2, we need a matrix expression for the various tableaux. We will find it helpful to consider a slightly more general problem, that of regression of one *or more* dependent variables, written as a matrix Y, on the same set of n independent variables, X. Then the first tableau of Table 2–2 would have the form

$$\begin{pmatrix} X'X & X'Y \\ Y'X & Y'Y \end{pmatrix}. \tag{2–1.5}$$

From the discussion of partitioned matrices, we can see that starting the Gauss-Jordan process on this matrix, we obtain a tableau of the form

$$\begin{pmatrix} I & B \\ 0 & C \end{pmatrix}, \tag{2–1.6}$$

where B is the matrix of regression coefficients,

$$B = (X'X)^{-1}X'Y. \tag{2–1.7}$$

The matrix C is the result of subtracting from the second group of rows of the matrix in (2–1.5) the linear combinations of the first n rows which will give the 0-matrix in the lower left corner of (2–1.6). Namely, we subtract*

$$\left(Y'X(X'X)^{-1}\right)(X'X, X'Y) = (Y'X, Y'XB).$$

Therefore

$$C = Y'Y - Y'XB. \tag{2–1.8}$$

To appreciate the significance of this matrix C, let us consider the matrix R of the residuals or "misses" of the several equations

$$R = Y - XB. \tag{2–1.9}$$

Then

$$R'R = (Y' - B'X')(Y - XB) = Y'Y - Y'XB - B'X'Y + B'X'XB. \tag{2–1.10}$$

Substitution of (2–1.7) for the last B on the right shows that the last term on the right is

$$B'X'XB = B'(X'X)(X'X)^{-1}X'Y = B'X'Y.$$

Therefore, the last two terms on the right of (2–1.10) cancel and leave

$$R'R = Y'Y - Y'XB = C. \tag{2–1.11}$$

---

* Bear in mind that in any matrix product, AB, the rows of the product are linear combinations of the rows of the second matrix, B.

Hence, in the tableau depicted by (2–1.6), *the C-matrix is the matrix of the sum of squares and cross products of the residuals of the regression R'R.* This fact has at least three important computational consequences.

1) *Use of deviations from means.* When the first independent variable is a constant vector of 1's, as it is in Table 2–1 and as it usually is, then, as we noted, the regression coefficients of all the other variables on it are merely the means of their respective variables. Therefore, by interpreting X in Eq. (2–1.11) as only the x_1-column of Table 2–1, while interpreting Y of (2–1.11) as the x_2-, x_3-, and y-columns of Table 2–1, we see that, except for the first row and column, Tableau 2 of Table 2–2 can be calculated as the sums of squares and cross products of the deviations of all the variables from their means. The calculation of Tableau 2 by this method is shown in the last four columns of Tables 2–1 and 2–2. This way takes more work than does the pivot-operations way, but it generally has the advantage of greater numerical accuracy. For, as the reader will note, the numbers in Tableau 2 are considerably smaller than those in Tableau 1. This contraction, which is common to all regression problems, would cause no problem if Tableaux 1 and 2 were calculated without rounding error. In practice, the numbers in Tableau 1 may run to ten digits or more, and therefore lead to rounding in many electronic computers. Small percentage errors in the first Tableau 1 become relatively much larger in the second tableau. We can avoid the big numbers of Tableau 1 and the resulting rounding errors by working with the deviations from means.

2) *Calculations of R^2, the coefficient of multiple determination.* This common measure of how well the independent, explanatory variables succeed in explaining the dependent one is defined as the fraction of the variance of the dependent variable explained by the independent ones. More precisely, the variance, s_y^2, of the dependent variable is defined by

$$s_y^2 = \frac{1}{T} \sum_{t=1}^{T} (y_t - \bar{y})^2,$$

and the "unexplained," or residual variance, is defined by

$$s_r^2 = \frac{1}{T} r'r,$$

where $r = y - Xb$. The "explained" variance is then defined as the difference, $s_y^2 - s_r^2$, and R^2 is defined by

$$R^2 = \frac{s_y^2 - s_r^2}{s_y^2} = 1 - \frac{s_r^2}{s_y^2} = 1 - \frac{r'r}{\sum_{t=1}^{T} (y_t - \bar{y})^2}.$$

Table 2-3

REGRESSION WITH INVERSION

Tableau 1	5	25	25	75
	25	225	85	380
	25	85	171	415
	75	380	415	1189
Tableau 2	0.2	5	5	15
	−5	100	−40	5
	−5	−40	46	40
	−15	5	40	64
Tableau 3	0.45	−0.05	7	14.75
	−0.05	0.01	−0.4	0.05
	−7	+0.4	30	42
	−14.75	−0.05	42	63.75
Tableau 4	2.0833	−0.1413	−0.2333	4.95
	−0.1413	0.01532	0.0133	0.61
	−0.2333	0.0133	0.0333	1.4
	−4.95	−0.61	−1.4	4.95

third columns and rows interchanged. Applying again the reasoning supplied by the reader at the end of the last paragraph, we see that

$$\left(\frac{\partial b_1}{\partial b_2}, \frac{\partial b_2}{\partial b_2}, \frac{\partial b_3}{\partial b_2}\right) = \left(\frac{-0.1413}{0.0152}, \frac{0.0152}{0.0152}, \frac{0.0133}{0.0152}\right) = (-9.3, 1, 0.875).$$

In general, *to obtain the vector of partial derivatives with respect to b_i, we just divide the ith column of the inverse by its diagonal element.*

If we change the value of the regression coefficient of, say, x_2 by the amount Δb_2 from the least-squares value, b_2, the resulting equation becomes

$$\hat{y} = \left(b_1 + \Delta b_2 \frac{\partial b_1}{\partial b_2}\right) + (b_2 + \Delta b_2)x_2 + \left(b_3 + \Delta b_2 \frac{\partial b_3}{\partial b_2}\right)x_3.$$

For example, if we wish to make the coefficient of x_2 zero, we set

$$\Delta b_2 = -0.61$$

and obtain

$$\hat{y} = [4.95 + (-0.61)(-9.3)] + [1.4 + (-0.61)(0.875)]x_3 = 10.6 + 0.87x_3.$$

In practice, the method of least squares often gives unreasonable values for the coefficients in an equation, although another equation with sensible coefficients would fit the data almost as well. Forcing one key coefficient to a reasonable value frequently makes the others reasonable, but lowers R^2 only slightly. The availability of these partial derivatives facilitates this combination of economic judgment with the requirement that the equation fit the data fairly well.

A further important use of the inverse matrix will be shown in the next section.

PROBLEMS

Save the solution of the first two problems for use in Section 2–2.

1. Given the data in Table 2–4, compute the regression of y on x_1, on x_1 and x_2, on x_1, x_2, and x_3, and on x_2 and x_3. Use the method of derivatives for the last computation. Find R^2 for each of the first three regressions.

Table 2–4

X_1	X_2	X_3	y
1	3	6	11
1	7	4	20
1	5	9	17
1	1	5	9
1	9	4	24
1	5	8	15

2. One theory of the determination of the rate of increase in the money wage rate states that

$$y_t = b_1 x_{t1} + b_2 x_{t2} + b_3 x_{t3} + \epsilon_t,$$

where

y_t = annual average rate of increase of straight-time hourly earnings in key industries during the tth wage round (in cents per hour);

x_{t1} = a dummy variable equal to 1 for all t;

x_{t2} = profit rate at the beginning of the tth wage round (more precisely, quarterly after-tax profits plus depreciation, all divided by stockholders' equity);

x_{t3} = average rate of unemployment in durable goods industries during the tth wage round (in percent).

A *wage round* is the time between two clusters of pattern-setting bargains. For five postwar rounds, we have the data listed in Table 2–5.

Estimate b_1, b_2, and b_3. Find R^2. Work with deviation from means. (This problem is taken from Eckstein and Wilson, "Determination of Money Wages in American Industry," *Quarterly Journal of Economics*, **76**, August 1962, p. 389. Reprinted by permission.)

Table 2-5

t	x_{t1}	x_{t2}	x_{t3}	y_t
1	1	16.8	7.3	2.5
2	1	23.1	2.8	9.5
3	1	16.8	3.5	4.6
4	1	19.1	5.6	5.1
5	1	17.4	5.6	3.6

3. Show that $(AB)' = B'A'$.

4. In Table 2–3, each of Tableaux 2, 3, and 4 have the form

$$\begin{pmatrix} A & C \\ -C' & B \end{pmatrix},$$

where $A = A'$ and $B = B'$. Use partitioned matrices to prove that these tableaux will *always* have this form. Note that use of this fact can reduce the labor of calculation nearly fifty percent.

5. Note that it is not necessary to introduce the variables into the regression equation in the order x_1, x_2, x_3, etc. We could introduce them in any order, say x_1, x_3, x_2, by pivoting first in the first row, then in the third, then in the second. Rework the example of the text in this order. State the rule for choosing which variable to enter next so as to get the largest possible increase in R^2. This rule is automatically used in many computer programs. What reasons might there be for and against its use?

2-2 PROBABILISTIC PROPERTIES OF LEAST-SQUARES ESTIMATES

The method of least squares is frequently dressed up by postulating a probabilistic model behind it. To explain this model we need to recall a few definitions from statistics; we now give these in summary fashion.

Let $F(x)$ be the probability that a random variable ϵ is less than x. $F(x)$ is called the *probability distribution function of* ϵ. For example, if ϵ is the height of college freshmen, $F(6')$ is the probability that a freshman picked at random will be less than 6 ft tall. The derivative of $F(x)$,

$$f(x) = \frac{dF(x)}{dx},$$

is called the *probability density function* of ϵ. The probability that $a \leq \epsilon \leq b$, denoted by $P(a \leq \epsilon \leq b)$, is $\int_a^b f(x)\, dx$. The *expected value* of a function $g(\epsilon)$ of ϵ, $E(g(\epsilon))$, is defined as

$$E(g(\epsilon)) = \int_{-\infty}^{\infty} g(x)f(x)\, dx.$$

Two of these expected values are important enough to have names of their own:

The mean $\bar{\epsilon}$ of ϵ is

$$E(\epsilon) = \int_{-\infty}^{\infty} xf(x)\, dx. \tag{2-2.1}$$

The variance σ_{ϵ}^2 of ϵ is

$$E((\epsilon - \bar{\epsilon})^2) = \int_{-\infty}^{\infty} (x - \bar{\epsilon})^2 f(x)\, dx. \tag{2-2.2}$$

The standard deviation of ϵ is

$$\sigma_{\epsilon} = \sqrt{\sigma_{\epsilon}^2}.$$

Two random variables, ϵ_i and ϵ_j, may be interrelated. In this case, we say that a function $f(x_i, x_j)$ is their *joint probability density function* if

$$P\begin{pmatrix} a_i \le \epsilon_i \le b_i \\ \text{while} \\ a_j \le \epsilon_j \le b_j \end{pmatrix} = \int_{a_i}^{b_i} \int_{a_j}^{b_j} f(x_i, x_j)\, dx_i\, dx_j.$$

The expected value of a function, $g(\epsilon_i, \epsilon_j)$, of two random variables is defined by

$$E[g(\epsilon_i, \epsilon_j)] = \int_{-\infty}^{\infty} \int_{-\infty}^{\infty} g(x_i, x_j) f(x_i, x_j)\, dx_i\, dx_j. \tag{2-2.3}$$

An important special case is the *covariance* σ_{ij} of ϵ_i and ϵ_j, defined by

$$\sigma_{ij} = E[(\epsilon_i - \bar{\epsilon}_i)(\epsilon_j - \bar{\epsilon}_j)],$$

where

$$\bar{\epsilon}_i = E(\epsilon_i) = \int_{-\infty}^{\infty} \int_{-\infty}^{\infty} x_i f(x_i, x_j)\, dx_i\, dx_j.$$

An important property of the expected value is that if a_1 and a_2 are constants, then, as a consequence of (2-2.3),

$$E(a_1\epsilon_1 + a_2\epsilon_2) = a_1 E(\epsilon_1) + a_2 E(\epsilon_2). \tag{2-2.4}$$

If $f(x_i, x_j)$ can be factored and written as $f(x_i, x_j) = f^i(x_i)f^j(x_j)$, where f^i and f^j are the density functions of ϵ_i and ϵ_j, then ϵ_i and ϵ_j are said to be *independent*. If they are independent, the reader may easily show that $\sigma_{ij} = 0$.

The postulate lying behind the statistical theory of least squares is that there exists a "true" vector β such that

$$y = X\beta + e, \tag{2-2.5}$$

where e is a vector of random variables, each with mean zero. If we regard the X-matrix as constant, then the least-squares regression coefficients, $b = (X'X)^{-1}X'y$, are *unbiased* estimates of β. That is, $E(b) = \beta$.

Proof

$$E(b) = E[(X'X)^{-1}X'(X\beta + e)] = \beta + E[(X'X)^{-1}X'e)]$$
$$= \beta + (X'X)^{-1}X'E(e) = \beta,$$

since $E(e) = 0$.

We can easily find the variances and covariances of the elements of b if we are willing to assume that the components of e have zero covariance and that all have the same variance, σ^2. In symbols, we have

$$E(ee') = \sigma^2 I_T, \tag{2-2.6}$$

where I_T denotes a T-by-T indentity matrix, and T is, as before, the number of observations.

Premultiplying both sides of (2–2.5) by X' and solving for β, we obtain

$$\beta = (X'X)^{-1}(X'y - X'e);$$

hence

$$b - \beta = (X'X)^{-1}X'y - (X'X)^{-1}(X'y - X'e) = (X'X)^{-1}X'e,$$

and

$$E(b - \beta)(b - \beta)' = E[(X'X)^{-1}X'ee'X([X'X]^{-1})']$$
$$= E[(X'X)^{-1}X'ee'X(X'X)^{-1}]$$
$$\text{(since } (X'X)^{-1} \text{ is symmetric)}$$
$$= (X'X)^{-1}X'E(ee')X(X'X)^{-1}$$
$$= \sigma^2(X'X)^{-1}. \tag{2-2.7}$$

The diagonal elements of the matrix $\sigma^2(X'X)^{-1}$ give the variances of $b_1, \ldots, b_n$, and the off-diagonal elements give their covariances.

Generally, σ^2 is not known, but is estimated. Since $E(e'e) = T\sigma^2$ and the vector of *residuals*, $r = y - Xb$, resembles $e = y - X\beta$, we may expect to be able to estimate σ^2 from $r'r$. We shall show that $E(r'r) = (T - n)\sigma^2$, where n is the number of independent variables, so that $r'r/(T - n)$ is an unbiased estimate of σ^2. To prove this result we need the concept of the *trace* of a matrix.

Definition. The trace of a square matrix is the sum of its diagonal elements:

$$\text{trace of } A = \text{tr } A = \sum_{i=1}^{n} a_{ii}.$$

If A is n by m and B is m by n, then tr $AB = $ tr BA, for the ith diagonal element of AB is $\sum_{j=1}^{m} a_{ij}b_{ji}$, so

$$\text{tr } AB = \sum_{i=1}^{n}\sum_{j=1}^{m} a_{ij}b_{ji} = \sum_{j=1}^{m}\sum_{i=1}^{n} b_{ji}a_{ij} = \text{tr } BA. \qquad (2\text{--}2.8)$$

Now, to prove that $E(r'r) = (T - n)\sigma^2$, we have

$$r = y - X(X'X)^{-1}X'y = X\beta + e - X(X'X)^{-1}X'(X\beta + e)$$
$$= e - X(X'X)^{-1}X'e.$$

Let $B = X(X'X)^{-1}X'$ and note that

$$B = B', \qquad B'B = BB = B,$$

and

$$\text{tr } B = \text{tr } X(X'X)^{-1}X' = \text{tr } X'X(X'X)^{-1} = \text{tr } I_n = n, \qquad (2\text{--}2.9)$$

where I_n is n by n. Then $r = e - Be$, and

$$
\begin{aligned}
E(r'r) &= E(e'e - e'Be - e'B'e + e'B'Be) \\
&= E(e'e - e'Be) && (2\text{--}2.10) \\
&= T\sigma^2 - E(e'Be) && \text{(Bear in mind that } e'e \text{ is a scalar, while } ee' \text{ is} \\
& && \quad \text{a } T\text{-by-}T \text{ matrix.)} \\
&= T\sigma^2 - E(\text{tr } e'Be) && (\text{Tr } e'Be = e'Be, \text{ since the latter is a scalar.)} \\
&= T\sigma^2 - E(\text{tr } ee'B) \\
&= T\sigma^2 - \text{tr }\left(E(ee')B\right) \\
&= T\sigma^2 - \text{tr }\sigma^2 I_T B = T\sigma^2 - \sigma^2 \text{ tr } B \\
&= (T - n)\sigma^2. && (2\text{--}2.11)
\end{aligned}
$$

Consequently, $s^2 = r'r/(T - n)$ is an unbiased estimate of σ^2.

The theoretical *multiple correlation coefficient* is defined as

$$\rho = \sqrt{1 - \sigma^2/s_y^2},$$

where

$$s_y^2 = \sum_{i=1}^{} \frac{(y_i - \bar{y})^2}{T - 1}$$

and $\bar{y}$ is the mean of the y's. An unbiased estimate of the square of the theoretical correlation coefficient is given by

$$\bar{R}^2 = 1 - (s^2/s_y^2);$$

$\bar{R}^2$ is sometimes called the *coefficient of multiple determination* adjusted for degrees of freedom.

Applying the results of this section to the example of Section 2–1 gives $s^2 = 4.95/(5 - 3) = 2.47$,

$$\bar{R}^2 = 1 - \frac{(4.95)(5 - 1)}{(5 - 3)(64)} = 1 - 0.15 = 0.85,$$

and the following standard errors for the regression coefficients:

$$\sigma_{b_1} = \sqrt{(2.47)(2.08)} = 2.26,$$
$$\sigma_{b_2} = \sqrt{(2.47)(0.01532)} = 0.20,$$
$$\sigma_{b_3} = \sqrt{(2.47)(0.0333)} = 0.28.$$

It is standard practice to report a regression equation with the standard errors of the coefficients placed below them in parentheses. Our equation for the example in Section 2–1 would therefore appear as

$$y = \begin{matrix} 4.95 \\ (2.26) \end{matrix} + \begin{matrix} 0.61x_2 \\ (0.20) \end{matrix} + \begin{matrix} 1.40x_3, \\ (0.28) \end{matrix} \qquad \bar{R}^2 = 0.85.$$

PROBLEMS

1. Find $\bar{R}^2$ and the standard deviations of the b's for Problem 1 of Section 2–1.

2. Do the same for Problem 2 of Section 2–1.

3. Find the standard deviation of $c'b$, where c' is a row vector of known constants and b is, of course, the column of regression coefficients. [Assume that (2–2.6) is satisfied.]

4. Show that if $b^* = Ay$ (where A is an n-by-T matrix of constants) is any *unbiased* estimate of β, then $AX = I$. Next show that the variance-covariance matrix of b^* is $\sigma^2 AA'$. Finally, show that

$$[(X'X)^{-1}X' - A][(X'X)^{-1}X' - A]' = AA' - (X'X)^{-1},$$

and explain why the variance of each element of b^* is at least as large as that of the corresponding element of b, the least-square estimate.

CHAPTER 3

COMPUTER PROGRAMMING BY FORTRAN

3-1 A LEAST-SQUARES REGRESSION PROGRAM

Computers have invaded applied economics so thoroughly that an understanding of basic programming has become almost a necessity. Regression analysis provides an excellent introductory example, and, by following through the example, the reader will strengthen his grasp of regression computations. Programs are easy to write, and though occasionally one finds someone else's program usable, most problems seem to require some original programming.

This regression program is written in FORTRAN, a language which is a compromise between the natural language of machines and that of mathematicians. The result is still comprehensible to the machine, but is also, let us hope, readily understandable to all who have read this far. Our discussion, neither complete nor authoritative, does cover the essentials. After spending two hours with the FORTRAN reference manual for a particular machine, the reader should know all the rules, though not the ropes.

The inside of a computer is rather like a post office with a large number of pigeon holes. In the computer, each pigeon hole can hold one number; in most machines, the number may have up to eight digits.† The first thing the computer does when confronted with a program such as that shown in Fig. 3–1, is to look it over for the names of variables, to make a name tag for each of them, and to place the tag on a pigeon hole. In our program, the variables X, A, and P have subscripts—A(I, J) is the FORTRAN way of writing A_{ij}, and P(I) corresponds to P_i—so a DIMENSION statement is necessary for the machine to know how many pigeon holes to save for these matrices. X, for example, is dimensioned as 50 by 8, so it requires 400

---

† In other machines, the size of the pigeon hole or "word" is variable; the programmer may choose whether he would like many small or few large holes.

46

pigeon holes, more properly called storage locations, and these will be labeled

$$X(1, 1), X(2, 1), \ldots, X(1, 2), X(2, 2), \ldots, X(50, 8).$$

(There is no harm in saving more space for a matrix than it needs, but woe to him who uses more space than he has saved.)

There are two fundamental differences between FORTRAN and usual mathematical notation. Once these differences are mastered, all the rest is similarity.

Difference 1. The name of a variable, such as PIVOT, AJI, X(1, 1), A(3, 5), or P(4), is the name of a storage location, *not* of an unchanging number. It stands for whatever is in the storage location at the moment.

Difference 2. An equal sign, =, means "store the quantity on the right of = in the storage location on the left."

Example
```
C = 0.0
C = C + 3.0
B = C
C = (B/2.) * C
```

In mathematics, the second statement is a contradiction. In FORTRAN it simply means "add 3 to the contents of C and then store the result in pigeon hole C again." The contents of C are now 3.0; the 0 formerly there is erased. The third statement stores the contents of C in B; the contents of C are unchanged. The fourth statement divides the contents of B by 2, multiplies the quotient by the contents of C, and then stores the result in C. The final contents are B=3, C=4.5. (The multiplication sign * must *not* be omitted as it often is in algebra.)

We shall use repeatedly statements of the sort

```
     DO 10 I = M, N
10   A(I) = 0.
```

The first statement, called a "DO" statement, instructs the machine: "DO everything you come to from here on until you have done the statement numbered 10. Do all this, first with I = M, then with I = M+1, then with I = M+2, and so on through I = N." After the DO "loop" shown here is completed, we would have A(M)=0, A(M+1)=0, ... , A(N)=0. A statement number appearing just to the left of the statement, for example, the 10 in the second statement above, is merely a name for that statement. Other statements, e.g., the DO statement above, refer to it by that name. It is not necessary to number all statements and the numbers do not have to be in order. Statement 10 could follow statement 50.

```
       SUBROUTINE REGRES
    6  COMMON NIV,NO,X
    8  DIMENSION X(50,8),A(8,8),PD(7)
   10  NC = NIV + 1
C      NIV IS NUMBER OF INDEPENDENT VARIABLES.
C      NO IS NUMBER OF OBSERVATIONS.
C      FORM THE CROSS-PRODUCT MATRIX, A.
   11  DO 25 I = 1,NC
   12  DO 25 J = I,NC
   13  A(I,J) = 0.
   14  DO 20 N = 1,NO
   20  A(I,J) = A(I,J) + X(N,I) * X(N,J)
   25  A(J,I) = A(I,J)
C      INVERSION OF A MATRIX
   30  DO 55 I = 1,NIV
   31  PIVOT = A(I,I)
   32  A(I,I) = 1.
C      DIVIDE PIVOT ROW BY PIVOT ELEMENT.
   33  DO 35 K = 1,NC
   35  A(I,K) = A(I,K)/PIVOT
C      REDUCE NONPIVOT ROWS.
   38  DO 45 J = 1,NC
C      SKIP PIVOT ROW.
   39  IF(J-I) 40,45,40
   40  AJI = A(J,I)
   41  A(J,I) = 0.
   42  DO 43 K = 1,NC
   43  A(J,K) = A(J,K) - A(I,K) * AJI
   45  CONTINUE
C      PRINT REGRESSION COEFFICIENTS.
   46  WRITE (6,47) I,(A(J,NC),J = 1,I)
   47  FORMAT(17H REGRES COEF WITH I3,11H VARIABLES./
      1(7F12.5) )
C      FIND PARTIAL DERIVATIVES OF REGRESSION
C      COEFFICIENTS.
   48  DO 51 K = 1,I
   49  DO 50 J = 1,I
   50  PD(J) = A(J,K)/A(K,K)
   51  WRITE (6,52) (PD(J), J = 1,I)
   52  FORMAT(7F12.5)
   55  CONTINUE
   60  RETURN
   61  END                                     Figure 3-1
```

```
C        READING AND CALLING PROGRAM FOR REGRESSION
         COMMON NIV,NO,X
         DIMENSION X(50,8)
C        READ THE NUMBER OF INDEPENDENT VARIABLES AND
C        THE NUMBER OF OBSERVATIONS.
    1    READ (5,5) NIV, NO
    5    FORMAT(2I3)
         NC = NIV + 1
C        READ THE X MATRIX, ONE ROW PER CARD.
         DO 10 I = 1,NO
   10    READ (5,12) (X(I,J),J = 1,NC)
   12    FORMAT(8F10.2)
         CALL REGRES
   15    GO TO 1
         END
```

Figure 3-1 (*cont.*)

Let us turn now to the regression program (Fig. 3–1). It will be punched on cards exactly as it appears here, one line per card, and is given to the machine in that form. Because the programming necessary for getting data in and out of the machine varies considerably from one installation to another and involves no logical principles, we skip it and assume that another program has read in the following:

NIV, the Number of Independent Variables,

NO,   the Number of Observations (T in the notation of Section 2–1),

X,   the matrix of independent variables plus the dependent variable in the last column [the matrix (X, y) in the notation of Section 2–1].

Such a reading program is given below REGRES. Comments on the reading program are provided in the appendix at the end of this chapter. When this information has been stored in the appropriate pigeon holes, the reading program will have the statement

CALL REGRES

and our program takes charge of the machine. Let us follow through, statement by statement, what it does. We repeat the program in pieces so that the student will not have to continuously refer to Fig. 3–1.

```
      SUBROUTINE REGRES
 6    COMMON NIV,NO,X
 8    DIMENSION X(50,8),A(8,8),PD(7)
10    NC = NIV + 1
C     NIV IS NUMBER OF INDEPENDENT VARIABLES.
C     NO IS NUMBER OF OBSERVATIONS.
C     FORM THE CROSS-PRODUCT MATRIX, A.
11    DO 25 I = 1,NC
12    DO 25 J = I,NC
13    A(I,J) = 0.
14    DO 20 N = 1,NO
20    A(I,J) = A(I,J) + X(N,I) * X(N,J)
25    A(J,I) = A(I,J)
C     INVERSION OF A MATRIX
30    DO 55 I = 1,NIV
31    PIVOT = A(I,I)
32    A(I,I) = 1.
C     DIVIDE PIVOT ROW BY PIVOT ELEMENT.
33    DO 35 K = 1,NC
35    A(I,K) = A(I,K)/PIVOT
```

STATEMENT ACTION
 NUMBER

6   Because NIV, NO, and X are listed in a COMMON statement here and in exactly the same COMMON statement in the program which originally read them, this program will look for them in exactly the same pigeon holes in which the reading program put them.

8   With this DIMENSION statement, NO must not exceed 50 and NIV must not exceed 7. Either may, of course, be less than its upper limit. X must have the same dimensions here as in the program which read and stored it.

10   NC, the Number of Columns in the X-matrix, is one greater than NIV.

C   A card with a C at the extreme left is a comment card. The machine skips it entirely, but it can remind the programmer on Monday morning what he was thinking of on Friday afternoon. Use them liberally.

11 From 11 to 25 we form the matrix $A = X'X$, that is, the matrix on the right of Eq. (2–1.4) or in Tableau 1 of Table 2–2. I is the number of the row of the element being calculated.

12 J is the number of the column of the element being calculated. Note that this DO terminates on the same statement, number 25, as did the previous one. The lower or "inner" DO must be completed, however, before the upper DO considers 25 to be finished. Thus, with I=1, J goes from 1 to NC; only then does I become 2, and J then again goes from 2 to NC, and so on. By starting J at I rather than at 1, and including statement 25, we take advantage of the fact that

$$A(I,J) = A(J,I),$$

so only one of them needs to be computed.

13, 14, 20 These three statements perform the summation

$$A(I,J) = \sum_{N=1}^{NO} X(N,I) * X(N,J)$$

25 With the calculation of A(I,J) now complete, A(J,I) is filled in equal to it.

The A-matrix now contains Tableau 1 of Table 2–3. We now proceed to derive the other tableaux of that table from Tableau 1.

30, 55 I is the row and column number of the pivot element. A CONTINUE statement may be used anywhere in the program. It does not cause any action, but serves as a sort of milepost. In this case, when "milepost 55" is reached, the DO of statement 30 has run its course.

31 The contents of the pivot position are stored in PIVOT for future use.

32 The 1 of the diagonal position of the identity matrix is placed where the pivot element was. This statement and statement 41 together generate the identity matrix which is converted into the inverse, but they generate it only as it is needed.

33, 35 These two statements divide the pivot row, including the 1 on the diagonal, by the pivot element.

```
C          REDUCE NONPIVOT ROWS.
38    DO 45 J = 1,NC
C          SKIP PIVOT ROW.
39    IF(J-I) 40,45,40
40    AJI = A(J,I)
41    A(J,I) = 0.
42    DO 43 K = 1,NC
43    A(J,K) = A(J,K) - A(I,K) * AJI
45    CONTINUE
C          PRINT REGRESSION COEFFICIENTS.
46    WRITE (6,47) I,(A(J,NC),J = 1,I)
47    FORMAT(17H REGRES COEF WITH I3,11H VARIABLES./
    1(7F12.5) )
C          FIND PARTIAL DERIVATIVES OF REGRESSION
C          COEFFICIENTS.
48    DO 51 K = 1,I
49    DO 50 J = 1,I
50    PD(J) = A(J,K)/A(K,K)
51    WRITE (6,52) (PD(J), J = 1,I)
52    FORMAT(7F12.5)
55    CONTINUE
60    RETURN
61    END
```

38 to 45   Statements 38 to 45 subtract A(I,J) times the pivot row from each nonpivot row J.

38   J is the number of the row from which the subtraction is made.

39   The general form of the IF statement is

IF(E) L, M, N

where E is some variable or expression made up of variables combined with +, −, *, or / signs, and L, M, and N are statement numbers. If E < 0, the machine takes its next instruction from statement L, if E = 0, from statement M, and if E > 0, from statement N. In our case, J − I = 0 when we get to the pivot row, and we skip to the CONTINUE statement at 45. When J ≠ I, we go to 40. This is a typical use of the CONTINUE statement.

40   The contents of A(J,I), the element in the intersection of the row from which the subtraction is made and the pivot col-

umn, are stored in a space we may call AJI. (We could call it anything, say XYZ, but AJI reminds us of what is in it.)

41   This puts the zero of the identity matrix in A(J,I). See discussion of statement 32 above.

42, 43   These statements perform the actual subtraction.

46   This statement is reached first when Tableau 2 of Table 2–3 is completed and, thereafter, at the completion of each tableau. It causes the computer to write onto the tape on its tape drive number 6 the value of I and the regression coefficients, which are in the first I positions of the last column of A. The format in which the writing is done is determined by statement 47. At the end of the problem, tape 6 is transferred to another machine and printed. This tape assignment is standard at most computing centers. See Fig. 3–2 for the results.

47   The "17H" means print the following 17 characters as they stand. The I3 provides 3 spaces for an Integer, in this case, I. The "11H" again prints the next 11 characters. The / starts a new line of printing. The 7F12.5 means print up to 7 numbers on a line, with twelve spaces allowed for each number, five of them to the right of the decimal.† See Fig. 3–2 for the printing.

48–52   These calculate the derivatives of the regression coefficients with respect to each other. No new principles are involved.

60   This statement returns control to the program which called REGRES.

61   END marks the physical end of the program, nothing more. It does not stop the machine.

Figure 3–2 gives the data for the example of Section 2–1 and the machine printing of the solution.

A few miscellaneous notes fill out a basic knowledge of FORTRAN.

1) Other than READ, the only essential type of statement not used above is

```
GO TO M
```

where M is a statement number. The machine takes its next instruction from M.

---

† The 1 preceding the second line of this statement is a continuation code, which indicates that a statement or declaration is so long that it exceeds the maximum character length for one line.

INPUT DECK

```
$DATA
  3   5
        1.00         10.00          5.00         17.00
        1.00          5.00          1.00         10.00
        1.00          0.00          6.00         12.00
        1.00         10.00          3.00         16.00
        1.00          0.00         10.00         20.00
```

COMPUTED RESULTS
(PARTIAL DERIVATIVES ARE GIVEN
BELOW THE COEFFICIENTS)

```
REGRES COEF WITH    1 VARIABLES.
    15.00000
     1.00000

REGRES COEF WITH    2 VARIABLES.
    14.75000      0.05000
     1.00000     −0.11111
    −5.00000      1.00000

REGRES COEF WITH    3 VARIABLES.
     4.95000      0.61000      1.40000
     1.00000     −0.06880     −0.11200
    −9.34783      1.00000      0.86957
    −7.00000      0.40000      1.00000
```

Figure 3-2

Example. If $A \leq 0$, set $E = 0$; if $A > 0$, set $E = A^2$.

```
        IF (A) 20, 20, 22
    20  E = 0.
        GO TO 25
    22  E = A ** 2.
    25  CONTINUE
```

Note that A ** B means A^B.

2) Names of variables may consist of from one to six letters or numbers. Use names beginning with I,J,K,L,M,N for subscripts and for the variable and its limits in DO statements.

DO 25 J = I, NO   *Correct* | DO 25 Y = H, CN   *Incorrect*

Storage location with such names, the roman numerals of computers, can take only integers. They are known as interger-mode variables and are handled by a special arithmetic and by special input-output statements. (Hence the I, for Integer, in statement 47.) For all variables which may take on fractional values, use names beginning with the other letters. They are called floating-point mode variables. Do not mix the two types in arithmetic expressions.

A = B/I   *Incorrect* | T = I   A = B/T   *Correct*

The statement T = I puts the contents of I into floating mode and stores them in T. (I = A drops the fractional part of A and stores the result in integer mode in I.) A constant written with a decimal is in floating mode; without a decimal, it is in integer mode. (Note the decimal in statements 32 and 41 and its absence in statement 10 in REGRES.)

3) A subscript may contain a constant addend, e.g., A(I+1), A(I−3). But we cannot write E = A(I+J), for J is not a constant. Instead we may set IPJ = I + J, then E = A(IPJ).

The reader is now prepared to write programs for any of the computations described in this book. The FORTRAN reference manuals for the various machines, rather undigestable documents without some previous introduction, explain fully the appropriate reading and writing statements and describe certain nonessential, but very convenient, features of the language. For example, one can get $A = \log_e X$ by writing A = ALOG(X), or $A = e^X$ by writing A = EXP(X), and similary, $A = \sqrt{X}$ from A = SQRT(X), without more ado. And there are more shortcuts.

PROBLEMS

1. Write a program to find the largest element and smallest element of a vector, A, which has N elements. N will never exceed 100. Assume that A and N are already in storage.

2. Write a program to form the matrix product $A = BC$, where B is L by M, and C is M by N. L, M, and N will all be less than 20.

3. Modify REGRES to make it compute $\bar{R}^2$ and the standard errors of the b's.

4. Modify REGRES so that if an intercept is desired, it will work with deviations from the means, and compute R^2. *Suggestion:* Put on the same card with NIV and NO a third number, N1. N1 is to be the number of the variable in the first column of the cards. When N1 = 2, the machine is to supply an intercept by working with the deviations from the means; when N1 = 1, the program is to work as at present. Between statements 10 and 11, N1 = 2

must cause the X-matrix to be converted to the matrix of deviations from means and the first row and column of A to be set up in Tableau 2 of Table 2–3. Other required changes are: statement 11 becomes DO 25 I = N1, NC, and statement 30 becomes DO 55 I = N1, NIV. In the reading program, statement 10 becomes READ 12, (X(I, J), J = N1, NC).

5. In addition to the modifications introduced in Problem 4, make REGRES benefit from the structure of the tableaux pointed out in Problem 4 of Section 2–1.

APPENDIX

REMARKS ON READING PROGRAM

The data from the data cards are first recorded on a tape which is then placed on tape drive number 5. Statement 1 reads the integers NIV and NO from the first data card in the columns specified by the format statement 5, namely NIV from the first three spaces, NO from the next three. In statement 5, I3 indicates an integer occupying 3 spaces; 2I3 means two such integers, one right after the other. (There are a total of 80 spaces on a card.) Statement 10 will be executed first with I = 1, then with I = 2, and so on, to I = NO. Each time, it reads a row, the ith row, of X from a card, in the format specified by statement 12. This statement, FORMAT (8F10.2), says that there must be 10 spaces allowed for each element, and that if no decimal is punched, the machine will assume that there are two places to the right of the decimal in each field. Punched decimals override the format specification on the location of the decimal. "J = 1, NC" means the same here as in a DO statement. Thus, we could accomplish the reading by

```
      DO 10 I = 1,NO
      DO 10 J = 1,NC
  10  READ (5, 12) X(I, J)
```

There is an important difference, however, between the program and this alternative, for every time the READ statement is encountered, it starts on a new card and from the beginning of the FORMAT statement. If the READ statement reads all it wants to read before reaching the end of the format, well and good; the remaining fields on the card are simply not read. Thus, this alternative program reads NO ∗ NC cards; the original reads only NO cards. (Obviously, the cards must be different to give the same result.) [If a READ statement comes to the end of the FORMAT before it is through reading, it goes back to the last open parenthesis in the FORMAT statement and on to the next card.] READ is a command to the machine to do something; FORMAT merely tells it where to find something *if* it wants it. WRITE statements works just like READ statements. For a full discussion of format statements and particularly of variable format statements, the reader should consult the FORTRAN manuals.

Programs may be stopped in two ways:

a) by a STOP statement,
b) by trying to read a card when there is no card.

Statements 15 and 1 together constitute the second method. We can do a number of regressions, one after another, but when they are all done and the data supply is exhausted, we stop.

CHAPTER 4

LINEAR PROGRAMMING

4-1 THE SIMPLEX MULTIPLIER METHOD OF LINEAR PROGRAMMING

Many economic problems may be cast in the following form:

$$\begin{aligned}
\text{Maximize} \quad & z = c_1x_1 + c_2x_2 + \cdots + c_mx_m \\
\text{subject to} \quad & a_1x_1 + \cdots + a_{1m}x_m = b_1, \\
& \quad \vdots \\
& a_{n1}x_1 + \cdots + a_{nm}x_m = b_n, \\
& x_1 \geq 0, \ldots, x_m \geq 0,
\end{aligned} \tag{4-1.1}$$

where $m > n$. In matrix form, the problem may be written as follows:

$$\begin{aligned}
\text{Maximize} \quad & z = cx \\
\text{subject to} \quad & Ax = b \quad \text{and} \quad x \geq 0.
\end{aligned}$$

(Here c is a row, x and b are columns.) Problems of this type are called *linear programming* problems. A vector which satisfies $Ax = b$ and $x \geq 0$ is called a *feasible solution*. The columns of A are called *activities* or *processes;* an activity, A_i, is said to be *used* in a solution, x, if $x_i > 0$; $z = cx$ is called the *objective* function.

Example. A manufacturer of ball bearings uses three types of machines in his operations: lathes, grinders, and presses, of which he has 8, 16, and 13, respectively. He can make four types of bearings. Each bearing of type 1 requires one minute on a lathe, three minutes on a grinder, and two minutes of the press's time, as shown by the first column in Table 4–1. The time required on the different machines by the other bearings is shown in the remaining columns of the table. The unit profits of the various types of bearings are 9, 8, 11, and 6 cents each for types 1, 2, 3, and 4, respectively. How many of each bearing should the firm produce per minute to maximize its profits?

Table 4–1

Time (in min) required on	Types of bearings			
	1	2	3	4
lathe	1	3	2	2
grinder	3	2	3	1
press	2	3	3	2

We can put this problem in the form of a linear programming problem by letting x_i be the output per minute of bearing type i. Then we have the following:

$$\text{Maximize} \quad z = 9x_1 + 8x_2 + 11x_3 + 6x_4$$

subject to

$$\begin{pmatrix} 1 & 3 & 2 & 2 \\ 3 & 2 & 3 & 1 \\ 2 & 3 & 3 & 2 \end{pmatrix} \begin{pmatrix} x_1 \\ x_2 \\ x_3 \\ x_4 \end{pmatrix} \leq \begin{pmatrix} 8 \\ 16 \\ 13 \end{pmatrix}, \qquad (4\text{–}1.2)$$

$$x_1 \geq 0, \quad x_2 \geq 0, \quad x_3 \geq 0, \quad x_4 \geq 0.$$

The first line of the constraints in (4–1.2) says that the number of lathe-minutes used each minute must be less than or equal to eight, the number of lathes. We use "less than *or* equal to" rather than "equal to," because it is not necessary to use all the lathes. The second and third lines place similar constraints on the use of grinders and presses. The nonnegativity restrictions on the x_i simply mean that the processes won't run backward and produce lathe, grinder, and press time out of bearings.

The problem expressed by Eq. (4–1.2), however, is still not quite a linear programming problem, because it has the $\leq$ sign instead of the $=$ sign found in Eq. (4–1.1). To get the $=$ sign, we need only introduce activities which consist of simply letting a lathe, grinder, or press stand idle. Such activities are often called *disposal* or *slack* activities. On introducing them, we find that problem (4–1.2) becomes

$$\text{maximize} \quad z = 9x_1 + 8x_2 + 11x_3 + 6x_4 + 0x_5 + 0x_6 + 0x_7$$

subject to

$$\begin{pmatrix} 1 & 3 & 2 & 2 & 1 & 0 & 0 \\ 3 & 2 & 3 & 1 & 0 & 1 & 0 \\ 2 & 3 & 3 & 2 & 0 & 0 & 1 \end{pmatrix} \begin{pmatrix} x_1 \\ x_2 \\ x_3 \\ x_4 \\ x_5 \\ x_6 \\ x_7 \end{pmatrix} = \begin{pmatrix} 8 \\ 16 \\ 13 \end{pmatrix}, \qquad (4\text{–}1.3)$$

$$\bar{x}_1 \geq 0, \quad x_2 \geq 0, \quad x_3 \geq 0, \quad x_4 \geq 0, \quad x_5 \geq 0, \quad x_6 \geq 0, \quad x_7 \geq 0.$$

Note that the levels of operation of the disposal activities are required to be nonnegative. What would the operation of one of them at a negative level mean?

The problem expressed by (4–1.3) is now exactly of the form (4–1.1). The method we shall use to solve it, known as the *simplex method*, rests on the following

Fundamental Theorem. If there is a feasible solution, x^0, to a given linear programming problem, then either there is a feasible solution using only linearly independent activities which gives at least as high a value for z as does x^0, or an infinite value of z is possible.

Before we prove the theorem, two remarks may be helpful.

Remark 1. The infinite value of the objective is a mathematical possibility; when it occurs, as it sometimes does, in economic problems, it of course merely indicates that there is a mistake in the formulation of the problem.

Remark 2. No more than n columns of A can be linearly independent, for A has only n rows. Though the number of sets of n linearly independent columns of A may be large, it is finite, for there are only a finite number of ways of selecting n things from a set of n things. Our theorem tells us, therefore, that the maximum value of z occurs at one of this finite number of feasible solutions of (4–1.1) which use no more than n activities. It is simply not necessary to look at solutions which use more activities. The theorem, therefore, greatly reduces the size of the haystack in which we must search for the needle.

Proof. Let x^0 be any feasible solution of the problem, that is, $Ax^0 = b$ and $x^0 \geq 0$. We wish to show that there exists a vector x using only linearly independent columns of A and such that $Ax = b$, $x \geq 0$, and $cx \geq cx^0$. If (and only if) the activities used by x^0 are linearly dependent, there exists a vector $y \neq 0$ such that $Ay = 0$, with $y_i = 0$ if $x_i^0 = 0$. If y satisfies these conditions, then so does $-y$, and hence we may choose y so that $cy \geq 0$. Then for any value of a scalar t,

$$A(x^0 + ty) = Ax^0 + tAy = b,$$

so $x^0 + ty$ is a feasible solution if all its elements are nonnegative. The value which it gives to the objective function is $c(x^0 + ty) = cx^0 + cty$. If $cy > 0$ and some element of y is negative, then, starting from $t = 0$, we can increase the value of the objective function by increasing t until some element of $x^0 + ty$ becomes zero. We have then found a feasible solution which gives a higher z but uses one activity less than x^0 uses. If $cy > 0$ and $y \geq 0$, then an infinite maximum value of z is possible. If $cy = 0$, we can make t either positive or negative to obtain a feasible solution using one activity less than the given solution and yielding the same z.

Unless an infinite z is possible, we can continue to eliminate one activity after another from the given solution until all the remaining ones are linearly independent. In the process, z never decreases, and the theorem is therefore proved.

A solution of the equation $Ax = b$ which uses only linearly independent activities is called a *basic* solution,* and the square matrix formed of the columns of A which it uses is called the corresponding *basis* and will be denoted by B. If the use-level vector, u^B, which is the solution of the equations $Bu = b$, is nonnegative, then the basis B is said to be *feasible*, for the corresponding solution† of $Ax = b$ is feasible.

The simplex method of linear programming consists of finding an initial feasible basis—one is often obvious—and then changing this basis by substituting, one at a time, an activity not in the basis for one formerly in it. Each activity entering the basis is chosen so that the substitution will increase the objective function, and the activity leaving the basis is chosen so that the new basis will remain feasible. The basis is somewhat like a car packed for a vacation. To put in one more box, you have to take out one which is already in and rearrange all the others.

The crux of the simplex method lies in the rules for choosing activities to enter and to leave the basis. To state and derive these rules, we need a little more notation. Let c^B be the row vector of elements of c corresponding to the columns of B,** and let $z^B = c^B u^B$ be the value of the objective function for the basic feasible solution corresponding to the basis B. Furthermore, we define π^B, called the vector of *simplex multipliers*, corresponding to the basis B, by the equation

$$\pi^B = c^B B^{-1}. \tag{4–1.4}$$

Lastly, we define v^B, called the vector of *simplex criteria*, by

$$v^B = c - \pi^B A. \tag{4–1.5}$$

We can now state the two basic rules of the simplex method.

Introduction Rule. Starting from the basic solution corresponding to B, the introduction of activity k into the solution will increase the value of

---

* The m-dimensioned geometric figure having the basic solutions as vertices is called a *simplex*, hence the name of the programming method we are describing.

† If A_i, the ith column of A, is not in B, then $x_i = 0$; if A_i is B_j, then $x_i = u_j^B$.

** If A_i is B_j, then $c_j^B = c_i$.

the objective function if (and only if) its simplex criterion,

$$v_k^B = c_k - \pi^B A_k,$$

is positive.

Proof. If activity k is to be used at the level t, then the use of levels of the activities in B must be adjusted "to make room for" t units of A_k within the constraints. More precisely, the use levels of the activities in B become a function of t, $u(t)$, which must satisfy the equation

$$Bu(t) + tA_k = b$$

or

$$u(t) = B^{-1}(b - tA_k) = u^B - tB^{-1}A_k. \tag{4-1.6}$$

The value of the objective function is therefore the following function of t:

$$\begin{aligned} z(t) &= c^B u(t) + c_k t \\ &= c^B(u^B - tB^{-1}A_k) + c_k t \\ &= c^B u^B + (c_k - c^B B^{-1}A_k)t \\ &= z^B + v_k^B t. \end{aligned} \tag{4-1.7}$$

If v_k^B is positive, it is clear that increasing t increases the objective function, as stated by the rule.

The economic interpretation of the simplex multipliers, π, is important. When we take as A_k one of the disposal activities, say the one which disposes of the ith resource, then $c_k = 0$, $\pi^B A_k = \pi_i^B$ and therefore, by (4-1.5), $\pi_i^B = -v_k^B$. But by (4-1.7), v_k^B is the amount by which the objective function goes up when the use of activity k goes up one unit. So if using activity k means simply disposing of resource i, it is natural to say that $-v_k^B = \pi_i$ is the *cost* of throwing away a unit of resource i and therefore the *value* of a marginal unit of this resource. Hence, for any A_k, $\pi^B A_k$ represents the opportunity cost of the resources used by that activity when the other opportunities for their use are confined to the activities in B. The Introduction Rule therefore becomes just common sense when stated in economic terms: start using activity A_k if its direct benefit, c_k, is greater than the opportunity cost, $\pi^B A_k$, of the resources it absorbs.

If $v_k^B > 0$, why can we not increase $z(t)$ as much as we like by taking sufficiently large values of t? The constraints $Ax = b$ remain satisfied for all values of t; but from (4-1.6) we can see that if some element of $B^{-1}A_k$ is positive, we cannot increase t indefinitely without making some element of $u(t)$ negative and thereby violating the $x \geq 0$ constraint. This fact gives rise to the second crucial rule.

Elimination Rule. If activity k enters the basis, and $p = B^{-1}A_k$, then column r of B must leave the basis, where r is chosen so that (a) $p_r > 0$, and (b) u_i^B/p_i is smaller for $i = r$ than for any other index which satisfies condition (a). More compactly,

$$\frac{u_r^B}{p_r} = \min_{[i \mid p_i > 0]} \left(\frac{u_i^B}{p_i} \right). \tag{4-1.8}$$

Proof. If we use the p-notation, Eq. (4-1.6) becomes

$$u(t) = u^B - tp. \tag{4-1.9}$$

As we increase t from zero, the solution generated remains feasible, though not basic, so long as $u(t)$ remains nonnegative. If $p_i \leq 0$, then $u_i(t)$ remains positive for all positive values of t, and therefore is of no concern for us. But if $p_i > 0$, we cannot make t larger than $t_i = u_i^B/p_i$ without making $u_i(t)$ negative. Therefore, at $t = t_r$, which, by (4-1.8), is the *smallest* of these ratios, the solution is still feasible and is again basic, for the rth column of B is no longer used, that is, it has been dropped from the basis. The rule is thus established. Economically interpreted, p is the rate of substitution between activity k and the activities already in the basis.

To start the calculations, we need to know an initial basic feasible solution. The Fundamental Theorem assures us that one exists if any feasible solution exists and an infinite maximum is not possible. Often, as in Eq. (4-1.3), one is obvious; in Eq. (4-1.3), we can just take $x_5 = 8$, $x_6 = 16$, $x_7 = 13$, and $B = (A_5, A_6, A_7)$. For the moment, let us assume that we have found such an obvious starting point. After describing the simplex method, we shall come back and see how it can be used to find an initial basis when none is obvious. With an initial B known, the calculations then go in the following order.

1) Find B^{-1} and $u^B = B^{-1}b$.

2) Calculate $\pi^B = c^B B^{-1}$, the simplex multipliers (the opportunity value of the resources).

3) Calculate $v^B = c - \pi^B A$, the simplex criteria (the opportunity costs of using each activity).

4) If $v^B \leq 0$, the optimal solution has been reached. If some element, v_k^B, is positive, choose A_k to introduce into the basis. If more than one element of v_k^B is positive, any one of the positive elements may be chosen, but experience shows it to be a good rule to choose as A_k the activity with the largest simplex criterion.

5) Calculate $p = B^{-1}A_k$ (the rates of substitution between A_k and the activities in B).

Table 4–2

THE SIMPLEX MULTIPLIER METHOD OF LINEAR PROGRAMMING

Tableau	Basis	c^B	p		u		Inverse		A_k
	$-\pi$			11	0	0	0	0	
0	A_5	0		2	8	1	0	0	2
	A_6	0		3	16	0	1	0	3
	A_7	0		3	13	0	0	1	3
	$-\pi$		0	3.5	-44	-5.5	0	0	
1	A_3	11	1	0.5	4	0.5	0	0	1
	A_6	0	0	1.5	4	-1.5	1	0	3
	A_7	0	0	0.5	1	-1.5	0	1	2
	$-\pi$		0	5	-51	5	0	-7	
2	A_3	11	0	2	3	2	0	-1	1
	A_6	0	0	3	1	3	1	-3	0
	A_1	9	1	-3	2	-3	0	2	0
	$-\pi$		0	0.33	-52.67	0	-1.67	-2	
3	A_3	11	0	1.33	2.33	0	-0.67	1	2
	A_5	0	1	0.33	0.33	1	0.33	-1	1
	A_1	9	0	-1.00	3.00	0	1	-1	2
	$-\pi$		0		-53	-1	-2	-1	
4	A_3	11	0		1	-4	-2	5	
	A_4	6	1		1	3	1	-3	
	A_1	9	0		4	3	2	-4	

6) Find the value of r such that

$$\left(\frac{u_r^B}{p_r}\right) = \min_{[i \mid p_i > 0]} \left(\frac{u_i^B}{p_i}\right).$$

7) Return to step 1 with the basis $(B_1, \ldots, B_{r-1}, A_k, B_{r+1}, \ldots, B_n)$.

We note that upon returning to step 1, we have to invert a matrix which differs from the one for which we already have the inverse in only one column, the rth. Therefore the method developed in Section 1–7 may be applied. We shall illustrate the entire procedure in a moment.

There remain, however, two theoretical points to be cleared up: first, to show that when $v^B \leq 0$, an optimum has indeed been reached, and, second,

SIMPLEX MULTIPLIER METHOD OF LINEAR PROGRAMMING 65

Table 4–3

	b			A					$-\pi^0$	$-\pi^1$	$-\pi^2$	$-\pi^3$	$-\pi^4$
	8	1	3	2	2	1	0	0	0	−5.5	5	0	−1
b, A	16	3	2	3	1	0	1	0	0	0	0	−1.67	−2
	13	2	3	3	2	0	0	1	0	0	−7	−2	−1
v^0	0	9	8	$\boxed{11}$	6	0	0	0					
v^1	−44	$\boxed{3.5}$	−8.5	0	−5	−5.5	0	0					
v^2	−51	0	2	0	2	$\boxed{5}$	0	−7					
v^3	$-52\frac{2}{3}$	0	−1.33	0	$\boxed{0.33}$	0	−1.67	−2					
v^4	−53	0	−2	0	0	−1	−2	−1					

to show that this state must be reached in a finite number of steps. Let us suppose that $v^B \le 0$ and that x^* is *any* feasible solution. Since

$$v^B = c - c^B B^{-1} A,$$

$v^B \le 0$ implies that $c \le c^B B^{-1} A$. Therefore, since $x^* \ge 0$,

$$cx^* \le c^B B^{-1} A x^* = c^B B^{-1} b = c^B u^B = z^B,$$

and we see that no feasible solution can give a higher value to the objective function than the one corresponding to B. The optimality condition will be reached in a finite number of steps, because there are only a finite number of bases, since, *if $t_r = u_r^B/p_r$ is always greater than zero*, the value of the objective function will increase with each change of basis. No basis can ever reappear. Therefore, optimality must be attained in a finite number of steps. The assumption that t_r is always greater than zero is called the "nondegeneracy assumption." In Section 4–4, we shall see that, with a slight refinement of the algorithm, we can be sure of always finding the optimum in a finite number of steps, even though sometimes $t_r = 0$.

Let us now observe how the above rules and procedure apply to the solution of the bearing manufacturer's problem as given in (4–1.3).

The computations are shown in Tables 4–2 and 4–3. In Table 4–2, the activities used by the solution are listed in the column headed "Basis." The column headed "c^B" shows the c's associated with these activities, and the one headed "u" shows the level of operations of these activities. The three columns headed "Inverse" show the inverse of the matrix made up of the activities in use. The first column of Table 4–3 lists the resource constraints, the b-vector. The remaining columns of the initial part of Table 4–3 show the available activities, with their c's displayed in the top row for reference.

The calculations proceed as outlined below.

Step 1. Find B^{-1} and u^B. Since the initial B is an identity matrix, finding B^{-1} is no problem. It is shown in the appropriate columns of the first tableau of Table 4–2. The corresponding u^B is shown in the u-column of Table 4–2.

Step 2. Calculate $\pi^B = c^B B^{-1}$. This is done by thinking of the c^B-column of Table 4–2 as a row and multiplying it by the matrix in the B^{-1}-columns of Table 4–2. The result is shown in the first $-\pi$-row of Table 4–2. In the u-column of this row, $c^B u^B$ gives the value of z^B.

Step 3. Calculate the simplex criteria $v = c - \pi^B A$. For these calculations, $-\pi$ is listed on the right of Table 4–3, and the result is shown in the v-row of that table. The first column of the v-row contains

$$-\pi b = -c^B B^{-1} b = -c^B u^B = -z^B,$$

the negative of the current value of the objective function. Comparison with the value found in Table 4–2 affords a check on the computations.

Step 4. If any of the v_k are positive, choose the activity with the largest positive v_k. Enter this activity in the A_k-column of Table 4–2.

Step 5. Multiply the B^{-1} matrix by A_k to obtain the column labeled "p" in Table 4–2.

Step 6. Calculate the ratios of the elements of the u-column over the corresponding elements of the p-column for all the positive elements of p. Choose that element p_r of p for which this ratio is smallest, mark it as a pivot element (with a box), and return to step 1.

In the second and subsequent tableaux, step 1 is performed in the following manner:

Step 1 revisited. To find the new B^{-1} and u^B, we apply the pivot rules (1–2.5) and (1–2.6). We pivot on p_r and carry out the pivot operation on the u- and B^{-1}-columns. The results are shown in Tableau 2 of Table 4–2. The resulting 1 and 0's in the p-column are shown in small figures just to make clear the operation which was performed; the space they would occupy if written full size may be needed later. In the "Basis" column of the new tableau, list the activities in the same manner as before, but put the new activity in the position where the eliminated activity was, i.e., in the row where the pivot element was. Similarly, list the c's corresponding to these activities beside them in the c^B-column.

Continue to go through the cycle of steps until no element of the v-vector is positive. The solution is then found in the u-column. Thus, from the last panel of Table 4–2 we find that the optimum is given by

$$x = (4, 0, 1, 1, 0, 0, 0).$$

A short cut is available for finding $-\pi$ in all the tableaux after the initial one. Namely, we can enter the simplex criterion of A_k in the intersection of the $-\pi$-row and the p-column of Table 4–2 and then carry through the pivot operation on this row just as on any other row. The justification of this short cut is quickly seen if we note that

$$\begin{pmatrix} 1 & c^B \\ 0 & B \end{pmatrix}^{-1} = \begin{pmatrix} 1 & -c^B B^{-1} \\ 0 & B^{-1} \end{pmatrix} = \begin{pmatrix} 1 & -\pi^B \\ 0 & B^{-1} \end{pmatrix}. \tag{4–1.10}$$

We may therefore think of the entries in the "Inverse" columns of Table 4–2, including the $-\pi$-row of these columns, as the n right-hand columns of the inverse of the "augmented" matrix

$$\begin{pmatrix} 1 & c^B \\ 0 & B \end{pmatrix}.$$

As we replace the $(r + 1)$-column of this matrix,

$$\begin{pmatrix} c_r^B \\ B_r \end{pmatrix},$$

by the new column,

$$\begin{pmatrix} c_k \\ A_k \end{pmatrix},$$

we can, of course, calculate from the old inverse the first row of the new inverse in exactly the same way as we would calculate any other (nonpivot) row, namely, by the pivot rules. By (4–1.10), the pivot column for changing the inverse of the augmented matrix is

$$\begin{pmatrix} 1 & -c^B \\ 0 & B \end{pmatrix}^{-1} \begin{pmatrix} c_k \\ A_k \end{pmatrix} = \begin{pmatrix} c_k - \pi^B A_k \\ B^{-1} A_k \end{pmatrix} = \begin{pmatrix} v_k \\ p \end{pmatrix}.$$

By entering this column in the p-column of Table 4–2 and carrying out the pivot operation on all $n + 1$ rows, we find not only the inverse of the new basis, but also its corresponding simplex multipliers. Furthermore, we find that

$$\begin{pmatrix} 1 & c^B \\ 0 & B \end{pmatrix}^{-1} \begin{pmatrix} 0 \\ b \end{pmatrix} = \begin{pmatrix} -\pi b \\ u^B \end{pmatrix} = \begin{pmatrix} -z^B \\ u^B \end{pmatrix}.$$

Therefore, we can also calculate the new value of the objective function, as well as the use vector, resulting from a one-column change in the basis by applying the pivot rule to the entire u-column, including the $-\pi$-row.

In computing by hand, it is convenient to separate Table 4–3 along the dashed line and to slide the columns across the A-matrix as the v_k are computed. The "accumulate multiply" feature of most desk calculators greatly facilitates this part of the work. Computer programs often keep Table 4–2 in internal rapid-access storage, while Table 4–3, or rather the initial A-matrix, is stored on tape. Since internal storage is limited and tape storage virtually unlimited, the size problem which can be handled in this way is limited only by the number of restraints, for their number determines the size of the B^{-1}-matrix. The number of activities which can be handled is practically unlimited. Note that it is easy to add activities to a program after its computation has been started, but it is relatively complicated to add restraints.

If the problem given in the form of (4–1.1) does not have an obvious initial feasible solution, we can find one by the following auxiliary problem:

$$\text{Maximize} \qquad z^1 = -\sum_{i=1}^{n} y_i$$

$$\text{subject to} \qquad Ey + Ax = b,$$
$$y \geq 0, \quad x \geq 0,$$

where the E-matrix is defined by

$$E_i = \begin{cases} e_i & \text{if } b_i \geq 0, \\ -e_i & \text{if } b_i < 0. \end{cases} \tag{4–1.11}$$

Note that we have just added artificial activities, E, to the original problem and taken as the objective the minimization of the use of these artificial activities. An obvious initial solution to this problem is $y_i = b_i$ and $B = E$. Note also that $E^{-1} = E$. We then apply the simplex method to make z^1 as large as possible, that is, to make the sum of the y's as small as possible. Of course, z^1 cannot be made greater than 0, but when a solution is found which does make $z^1 = 0$, *this solution is a feasible solution of the original problem*, for it uses only the original activities. (If the maximum value of z is less than 0, the original problem has no feasible solution.)

For some problems, the natural formulation is "*minimize cx* subject to $Ax = b$ and $x \geq 0$." These minimization problems are easily converted to the equivalent maximization problem "maximize $-cx$," and the simplex method as described above is applicable.

We must emphasize one final point. Because of the Fundamental Theorem, the basic problem of linear programming is determining *which* activities should be used, not the level of their use. For once we know the basis, the levels of use can be found by a straightforward solution of linear equations. A problem should not be formulated as a linear programming problem unless it is essentially a matter of choice of a small number of activities from among a larger number of possible ones. If the question is at what levels to use certain activities, all of which are likely to be used, the problem is not one of linear programming. By no means are all maximization problems linear programming problems; there may be nonlinearities in the objective function or in the constraints which must be taken into account, or there may be more constraints which should be added. Before we start to calculate, it is always a good idea to ask whether the implications of the Fundamental Theorem make economic sense.

PROBLEMS

1. What would be the effect on the optimal production plan of the firm in the example of the text if the price of the second type of bearing increased (a) 3¢, (b) 1¢, (c) 2¢?

2. A cotton farmer has been persuaded by his county agent to consider diversification. A banker is willing to lend the farmer up to $5000 for constructing facilities for raising livestock. The resource requirements for the various processes the farmer considers are given below.

Process Resources unit	Dairy cows (1 cow)	Layers (100 hens)	Hogs (1 sow)	Cotton (1 acre)	Corn (1 acre)	Alfalfa (1 acre)
Labor (man-hours)	100	120	100	100	10	8
Land (acres)	3	0	0.5	1	1	1
Construction ($)	200	400	200	0	0	0

The unit returns are $300 per cow, $200 per 100 layers, $120 per sow, $180 per acre of cotton, $80 per acre of corn, and $60 per acre of baled alfalfa. (These returns are net of 5% interest on capital.) The farmer has 100 acres of land and 4500 man-hours a year of family labor available.

a) What should be the farmer's operating plan for the coming year?
b) The county agent points out that the farmer has forgotten about keeping cows on purchased food. This way of keeping a cow takes 85 hours, 2 acres, $350 of construction, and yields a return of $230. Should this process be used? [Do not do (b) until you have finished (a).]

(Adapted from J. E. Faris and W. W. McPherson, *Review of Economics and Statistics*, November 1957.)

3. A petroleum refinery can make gasoline and diesel fuel from two different raw stocks, A and B, by three different processes, as follows (all figures in gallons):

Yield of gasoline	4	2	2
Yield of diesel fuel	2	2	4
Input of Stock A	5	3	5
Input of Stock B	3	3	3

Of stocks A and B, 5 and 4 million barrels per day are available, respectively.

a) What process or combination of processes will be used at each ratio of diesel and gasoline prices (p_d/p_g) between zero and infinity? [Let $p_g = 1$, and write the objective function as $(2 + p)x_1 + (1 + p)x_2 + (1 + 2p)x_3$. Maximize first with $p = 0$, then study the effects of increasing p.]

b) Graph the production possibility curve (or transformation curve between gasoline and diesel fuel) for this firm.

You may find it useful to know that

$$\begin{pmatrix} 5 & 3 \\ 3 & 3 \end{pmatrix}^{-1} = \begin{pmatrix} \frac{1}{2} & -\frac{1}{2} \\ -\frac{1}{2} & \frac{5}{6} \end{pmatrix}.$$

4. Prove that if B is nonsingular, the matrix $(B_1, \ldots, B_{r-1}, A_k, B_{r+1}, \ldots, B_n)$ obtained by application of the Elimination Rule is also nonsingular.

5. Show that a simple change in the Introduction Rule provides an algorithm which *minimizes* cx subject to $Ax = b$ and $x \geq 0$.

6. Write a FORTRAN program to perform the simplex method calculations. Use X to denote the $(n + 1)$-by-$(n + 1)$ matrix in the columns labeled "u" and "Inverse" of Table 4–1. Use C, A, and P as names for the quantities C, A, and p of the text, and let LIST be a vector listing the activities in the basis in the order in which they occur. LIST corresponds to the "Basis" column of Table 4–2. Use L in place of the r in the text. Be sure that your rule for termination takes into account the fact that rounding error is likely to make simplex criteria of some of the basic activities positive even in the optimal basis. Have the program print the simplex criteria and multipliers at each stage. If you have access to a computer, use your program to solve Problem 2(a) above.

4–2 SIMPLEX MULTIPLIERS AND DUALITY

We have seen that in linear programming problems with disposal activities, the simplex multipliers associated with the basis B represent opportunity values of the resources relative to the opportunities presented by the activities in that basis. They are therefore often called "shadow prices" of the resources and $\pi_i^B b_i$ is the "imputed value" of the ith resource. The total value imputed to the various resources equals the value of the objective function:

$$\pi^B b = c^B B^{-1} b = c^B u^B. \tag{4-2.1}$$

Thus the total product or profit of a firm, $c^B u^B$, would be exactly exhausted in paying to each resource its imputed value.

The shadow prices, π, corresponding to the *optimal* basis have several additional important properties summarized by the following theorem:

Theorem 4–1. If the linear programming problem

$$\text{maximize} \qquad cx$$

$$\text{subject to} \qquad Ax \leq b, \quad x \geq 0$$

has a finite maximum, then there exists a row vector π such that

i) $\pi \geq 0$,

ii) $c - \pi A \leq 0$,

iii) $(c - \pi A)x^0 = 0$,

iv) $\pi(Ax^0 - b) = 0$, where x^0 is the optimal value of x.

Proof

1) $\pi \geq 0$.   This inequality follows from the fact that all of the simplex criteria of the optimal solution must be nonpositive and $v_i = -\pi_i$ for the disposal activities.   Economically interpreted, the relation merely states that the shadow prices are nonnegative.

2) $c - \pi A \leq 0$.   This inequality is true because $v = c - \pi A$, and at the optimum, $v \leq 0$.   In economic terms, it states that no activity produces a positive profit when it is charged for the resources it uses at their shadow prices.

3) $(c - \pi A)x^0 = 0$, where x^0 is the optimal x.   Combined with Property 2 and the fact that $x^0 \geq 0$, this equation asserts that $x_i^0 > 0$ only if $(c - \pi A)_i = c_i - \pi A_i = v_i$ is zero.   But the simplex criteria of all activities in the basis are always zero, for the simplex criterion of the ith activity in the basis is $c_i - c^B B^{-1} B_i = c_i^B - c_i^B = 0$.   The economic meaning is that at the optimum, no activity is used which yields a negative profit when charged shadow prices for the resources it consumes.

4) $\pi(Ax^0 - b) = 0$.   Because, by Property 1, $\pi \geq 0$, this equation says that if the ith disposal activity is in use, $y_i = (b - Ax^0)_i > 0$, then $\pi_i = 0$.   This assertion is again a result of the fact that the simplex criteria of activities in use are zero and $\pi_i = -v_i$.   Economically, a resource which is not fully utilized is free.

We have still not completely proved this theorem, because our proof that the simplex method would give an optimum with $v \leq 0$ in a finite number of iterations rested on the assumption that t_r in the Elimination Rule was always strictly positive so that a positive v_i could always be used to increase z. In Section 4-6, we will show that $v \leq 0$ can always be attained even if t_r is sometimes 0.

A knowledge of the shadow prices is useful in the solution of problems related to investment in resources. For instance, in the example of Section 4-1, we may ask how much the firm would be willing to pay to rent an additional grinder. From the first row of the last tableau of Table 4-2, we see that the shadow price of a grinder is 2 cents per minute. Hence, at any rental cost below 2 cents a minute, the firm would find it desirable to rent more grinders.

Linear programming problems come in pairs, a primal and a dual, as follows:

Primal	Dual
Maximize $\qquad cx$	Minimize $\qquad pb$
subject to $\quad Ax \leq b, \quad x \geq 0.$	subject to $\quad pA \geq c, \quad p \geq 0.$

Here p is a row vector. The importance of the dual arises from the following proposition:

Theorem 4-2 (*The Duality Theorem*). The vector, π, of simplex multipliers from the optimal stage of the primal is the solution of the dual, and the maximum value of the primal is equal to the minimum value of the dual.

Proof. From Theorem 4-1, $\pi \geq 0$ and $\pi A \geq c$, that is, π is a feasible solution of the dual. But if x is *any* feasible solution of the primal and p is *any* feasible solution of the dual, then

$$cx \leq pAx \leq pb,$$

where the first inequality follows from the facts that $c \leq pA$ and $x \geq 0$, while the second follows from $Ax \leq b$ and $p \geq 0$. Hence, no feasible solution of the dual can give to its objective function a value lower than the maximal value of the primal's objective function. But by Eq. (4-2.1), $cx = \pi b$, so π must be an optimal solution of the dual.   Q.E.D.

Solving the primal by the simplex method, therefore, automatically gives a solution for the dual.

Note that when the dual is put in the proper form for the simplex method,

$$\text{maximize} \qquad -b'p'$$
$$\text{subject to} \qquad -A'p' \le -c', \quad p' \ge 0,$$

it has a dual,

$$\text{minimize} \qquad -x'c'$$
$$\text{subject to} \qquad -x'A' \ge -b', \quad x' \ge 0,$$

and this dual is again the original primal,

$$\text{maximize} \qquad cx$$
$$\text{subject to} \qquad Ax \le b, \quad x \ge 0.$$

Theorem 4–2, therefore, implies that the solution of the dual in the proper form for the simplex method, as given above, automatically gives a solution to the primal.

The usefulness of this result lies primarily in the addition of restraints to the primal, for adding a restraint to the primal is equivalent to adding an activity to the dual. When, therefore, it is anticipated that a number of constraints may be added to the problem after its initial solution, it is advantageous to work with the dual.

PROBLEMS

1. In Problem 2 of Section 4–1, how much would the farmer be willing to pay for
   a) an additional man-hour of labor?
   b) an additional acre?
   c) a loan of an additional $100?
2. In Theorem 4–1, what difference would it make if some of the constraints were given as equations (rather than as inequalities) with no disposal activities in them?

4-3 THE FULL-MATRIX TRANSFORMATION
VERSION OF THE SIMPLEX METHOD

Because of the fundamental importance of the simplex method, we shall look at three different variants of it in this and the next two sections. The metamorphoses of the method reveal its essence more clearly than any one version can.

In the simplex multiplier method, as we change the basis, we keep always before us the current solution, u^B, and the inverse of the current basis. In

Table 4-4

The Full-Matrix Transformation (or Standard) Method of Linear Programming

Tableau	Basis	u	$B^{-1}A$						
0	v	0	9	8	11	6	0	0	0
	A_5	8	1	3	2	2	1	0	0
	A_6	16	3	2	3	1	0	1	0
	A_7	13	2	3	3	2	0	0	1
1	v	-44	3.5	-8.5	0	-5	-5.5	0	0
	A_3	4	0.5	1.5	1	1	0.5	0	0
	A_6	4	1.5	-2.5	0	-2	-1.5	1	0
	A_7	1	0.5	-1.5	0	-1	-1.5	0	1
2	v	-51	0	2	0	2	5	0	-7
	A_3	3	0	3	1	2	2	0	-1
	A_6	1	0	2	0	1	3	1	-3
	A_1	2	1	-3	0	-2	-3	0	2
3	v	-52.67	0	-1.33	0	0.33	0	-1.67	-2
	A_3	2.33	0	1.67	1	1.33	0	-0.67	1
	A_5	0.33	0	0.67	0	0.33	1	0.33	-1
	A_1	3.00	1	-1.00	0	-1.00	0	1	-1
4	v	-53	0	-2	0	0	-1	-2	-1
	A_3	1	0	-1	1	0	-4	-2	5
	A_4	1	0	2	0	1	3	1	-3
	A_1	4	1	1	0	0	3	2	-4

other words, we keep before us the representation of the I-matrix and the b-vector relative to the current basis. When we decide to introduce a new activity, A_k, into the basis, we must first find its representation relative to the current basis, $p = B^{-1}A_k$. The simplex method was discovered and first used in a somewhat different form; in this form, as we change the bases, we keep before us the representation of the entire A-matrix relative to the current basis. The application of this version of the simplex method to the example of Section 4-1 is shown in Table 4-4, which should be compared closely with Tables 4-2 and 4-3. The pivot rule, Eq. (1-7.6), assures us that when we carry the pivot operation across all columns of the table, we keep before us the representation of the entire A-matrix relative to the current basis.

The Introduction and Elimination Rules remain exactly the same as they were before, as does the calculation of the simplex criteria by the pivot operation on the v-row of the tableaux. Because the representation of the activity introduced relative to the current basis, $p = B^{-1}A_k$, is already available in the kth column of the table, its special calculation is not necessary. We can just use it where it is. The physical location of the pivot column, therefore, jumps about from tableau to tableau, but the numbers in the pivot column here are the same as those in the p-column of Table 4-2.

What grounds are there for choosing between the multiplier version and the full-matrix transformation version of the simplex method? The multiplier method was placed first in this book precisely because it focuses on the multipliers and leads directly to their economic interpretation. Because it emphasizes the role of the basis, it is also the version which is easiest to explain by the methods of matrix algebra developed in Chapter 1. As for the amount of calculation involved, the full-matrix transformation version is preferable unless there are (a) many zeros in the A-matrix and (b) several times as many activities as constraints. This version is preferable because the number of multiplications and additions required to calculate the simplex criteria by $v_j = c_j - \pi A_j$ is exactly the same as the number required to perform the pivot operation on a column in the full-matrix method, while the full-matrix version avoids the need for a special calculation of $p = B^{-1}A_k$. If, however, the A-matrix contains many zero entries—and it usually does in practice—the calculation of $-\pi A$ will be substantially reduced. After a few pivot operations of the full-matrix version, most of the zeros disappear. If A has a sufficiently high ratio of columns to rows, the multiplier method therefore has the advantage. See Problem 2 below.

PROBLEMS

1. Work Problem 2 of Section 4-1 by the full-matrix transformation method.
2. Let t be the average fraction of nonzero terms in the columns of the n-by-m matrix A. Calculate how many additions and multiplications or divisions are required for one step of the pivot operation of (a) the multiplier method, (b) the full-matrix method. If $t = 0.2$ and $n = 10$, how large does m have to be to make the multiplier method require the least amount of calculation?
3. Write a FORTRAN program for the full-matrix transformation method.

4-4 THE SIMPLEX METHOD FOR TRANSPORTATION PROBLEMS

The multiplier version and the full-matrix transformation version of the simplex method are really very much the same thing. The transportation version of the simplex method, however, offers a greater change in vantage

Table 4–5

SHIPPING COSTS, REQUIREMENTS, AND SUPPLIES

Port	Inland city				Supplies: s_i
	1	2	3	4	
1	10	5	6	7	25
2	8	2	7	6	25
3	9	3	4	8	50
Requirements: r_j	15	20	30	35	100

point and, therefore, greater perspective on the nature of the simplex theory. Let us consider the problem of shipping 100 carloads of bananas from three ports to four inland cities. The inland cities have requirements of 15, 20, 30, and 35 carloads, respectively, while the ports have supplies of 25, 25, and 50 carloads each. The cost of shipping from each port to each inland city is given by Table 4–5. What is the cheapest way of meeting the requirements of the inland cities?

To see that this question poses a linear programming problem, let us denote the shipments (in carloads) from port i to city j by x_{ij} and the cost of this shipment (per carload) by c_{ij}, the requirements at city j by r_j, the supply at port i by s_i, and the number of ports and cities by m and n, respectively. The problem then becomes

$$\text{minimize} \qquad \sum_{i=1}^{n} \sum_{j=1}^{n} c_{ij} x_{ij}$$

$$\text{subject to} \qquad \sum_{i=1}^{m} x_{ij} = r_j, \qquad \sum_{j=1}^{n} x_{ij} = s_i,$$

$$x_{ij} \geq 0.$$

Problems with this mathematical structure are known as "transportation problems." Under the faint disguise of double subscripts, we perceive in them the familiar visage of a linear programming problem with mn activities (one for each cell of Table 4–5) and $m + n$ constraints. Activity (i, j) consists of the shipment of one unit from port i to city j. One of the constraints is redundant and can be dropped, for if an allocation exhausts all the supplies and meets all but one of the requirements, it meets also that last requirement, since the sum of the supplies equals the sum of the requirements. Hence, any basis of this program has only $m + n - 1$ activities.

This problem can, of course, be solved by the methods we have already developed; but because of the simplicity of the constraints, the calculations become greatly simplified. In the first place, we can always find with ease

Table 4-6

Port	Inland city			Supplies
	1	3	4	
1	10	6	7	25
2	8	7	6	5
3	9	4	8	50
Requirements	15	30	35	80

a nontrivial initial basis. We begin by finding the smallest c_{ij} and then making the corresponding x_{ij} as large as possible, namely

$$x_{ij} = \min (s_i, r_j).$$

We then delete the binding constraint, and subtract this x_{ij} from the other nonbinding constraint. That is, if $x_{ij} = s_i$, we delete the s_i-constraint, and replace r_j by $r_j - x_{ij}$. Applied to Table 4–5, this step gives $x_{22} = 20$, and leaves the result shown in Table 4–6.

Repeating this procedure, we get the basic solution $x_{22} = 20$, $x_{33} = 30$, $x_{24} = 5$, $x_{14} = 25$, $x_{34} = 5$, $x_{31} = 5$. This solution is recorded in the u-column of Table 4–7, and the cells used are marked by an asterisk (*) in Table 4–8, Tableau 0, which repeats Table 4–5.

Note that it was not necessary to go through the usual pivot operations to find the solution corresponding to this basis. Subtraction was the only operation required, for the basis was *triangular*, that is, the rows and columns of the constraint matrix could be renumbered so that all elements to the right of the diagonal would be zero. In terms of Table 4–5, *there is at least one row or column* (for example, column 2) *which contains one basic x_{ij}; after deleting that row or column, there is at least one row or column* (column 4 in this case) *which contains only one basic x_{ij}; and after deleting that row or column, there is at least one row or column* (row 3 in this case) *which contains only one basic x_{ij}, and so on, until all the rows and columns have been deleted.* In the "Basis" column of Table 4–7, the number of the row or column deleted "by" the activity is underlined. Thus the first line, 2 2, means that x_{22} is the only basic variable in the second column.

The crucial fact about transportation problems is that any basis has this triangularity property. Let us suppose, to the contrary, that all rows and all columns of Table 4–7 contain two or more basic variables. Then if k is the total number of basic variables, $k \geq 2m$ and $k \geq 2n$, it follows that $2k \geq 2m + 2n$ or $k \geq m + n$. But we know that in fact $k = m + n - 1$, so some row or column must contain only one basic variable. (Every row

Table 4–7

Tableau	Basis	u	c	$\pi_{i\cdot}$	$\pi_{\cdot j}$	$A_k = Bp$	p
	2 2	20	2	-2	4	$1 = p_{22}$	1
	3 3	30	4	0	4	$0 = p_{33}$	0
1	2 4	5	6	-2	8	$0 = p_{24} + p_{22}$	-1
	1 4	25	7	-1	8	$0 = p_{14}$	0
	3 4	5	8	0	8	$0 = p_{34} + p_{14} + p_{24}$	1
	3 1	15	9	0	9	$0 = p_{31}$	0
	3 1	5	9	1	8	$= p_{31}$	
	1 4	25	7	1	6	$= p_{14}$	
2	3 3	30	4	1	3	$= p_{33}$	
	3 2	5	3	1	2	$= p_{32} + p_{33} + p_{31}$	
	2 2	15	2	0	2	$= p_{22} + p_{32}$	
	2 4	10	6	0	6	$= p_{24} + p_{14}$	

Table 4–8

SIMPLEX CRITERIA

Tableau	Origin	Destination				s_i (or $\pi_{i\cdot}$)
		1	2	3	4	
	1	10	5	6	*7	25
0	2	8	*2	7	*6	25
	3	*9	3	*4	*8	50
	r_j	15	20	30	35	$\pi_{i\cdot}$
	1	2	2	3	*0	-1
1	2	1	*0	5	*0	-2
	3	*0	*-1	*0	0	0
	$\pi_{\cdot j}$	9	4	4	8	
	1	1	2	2	0	1
2	2	0	0	4	0	0
	3	0	0	0	1	1
	$\pi_{\cdot j}$	8	2	3	6	

$$v_{ij} = c_{ij} - (\pi_{i\cdot} + \pi_{\cdot j})$$

and every column must have at least one basic variable in order to satisfy the constraints.) This fact means that in the transportation problem, instead of inverting the basis, we can simply find the triangular order of the variables, and we easily find this order by following the above deletion process.

In the simplex method, we need B^{-1} for two purposes: to find the simplex multipliers, and to find the representation of the new activity relative to the old basis. Let us see how we can use triangularity to solve both problems. Let us denote the simplex multipliers on r_j and s_i by $\pi_{.j}$ and $\pi_{i.}$, respectively. Then the simplex criterion of activity ij is

$$v_{ij} = c_{ij} - (\pi_{i.} + \pi_{.j}). \qquad (4\text{-}4.1)$$

Table 4-7, Tableau 1, shows the calculation of the $\pi_{i.}$ and $\pi_{.j}$ from the fact that the simplex criteria of the basic activities are zero. We start from the bottom of the tableau and work up. We may assume that s_3 was the redundant constraint and therefore that $\pi_{3.} = 0$ in the $\pi_{i.}$-column of Tableau 1. Then since

$$v_{11} = c_{31} - (\pi_{3.} + \pi_{.1}) = 9 - (0 + \pi_{.1}) = 0,$$

we have $\pi_{.1} = 9$, as shown in the last line of the $\pi_{.j}$-column of Tableau 1. Moving up one line, we calculate $\pi_{.4} = 8$ and record the value in the $\pi_{.j}$-column in all rows in which $j = 4$ in the basis column (namely, in the third and fourth lines of the tableau). Then we move up another line and solve for $\pi_{1.}$, and so on, up to the top. The triangularity assures us that each equation will contain only one unknown.

Table 4-8 shows these simplex multipliers in the margins of Tableau 1, and the interior of the tableau contains the simplex criteria of the activities. Since we are minimizing instead of maximizing, we look for a negative simplex criterion and find only $v_{32} = -1$. Therefore x_{32} must enter the basis. To determine which activity is to be eliminated, we must find the representation of the column of x_{32} in the constraint matrix relative to the present basis. We write this column in the A_k-column of Table 4-7. In this table, the constraints are listed in triangular order, as indicated by the underlining in the basis columns. Thus, in Tableau 1, the order of the constraints is $r_2, r_3, s_2, s_1, r_4, r_1$. The column of x_{32} in the constraint matrix has a 1 in the s_3- and r_2-equations; the s_3-equation happens (quite by accident) to be the one which we dropped as redundant, so the x_{32}-column is as shown in the table. In the Bp-column of Table 4-7 is shown the sum of all the basic variables which enter a particular constraint. Because of triangularity, if we start solving these equations from the top, there will be only one new unknown in each equation, and by addition and subtraction, we can solve for the representation of the new activity relative to the old basis. The solution appears in the p-column.

The Elimination Rule is unchanged, and we see that x_{34} must be eliminated. We now know the new basis; its triangulation is shown in the basis column of Tableau 2, its solution, obtained by pivoting, appears in the u-column, and its simplex multipliers are shown in the π_i- and π_j-columns. Finally, its simplex criteria are given in Tableau 2 of Table 4–8, and we see that the solution is optimal.

PROBLEMS

1. Why do we find triangularity in solving for the simplex multipliers by working *up* the table, while in solving for p, we find it by working *down* the table?

2. Show that the p-vector will always contain only the numbers 1, -1, and 0. [*Suggestion:* Think of the constraints in a rectangular form.]

3. In the problem in the text, change c_{34} to 3 and solve from the beginning.

4. Write a FORTRAN program for the solution of transportation problems. In addition to a two-column LIST matrix, you will need a column which might be called MARK to indicate which element in the basis column is underlined.

4–5 THE DUAL SIMPLEX METHOD AND
MIXED INTEGER PROGRAMMING

Our final version of the simplex algorithm deals with the problem of how the solution changes with variations in the b-vector of the constraints $Ax = b$. To ascertain the sensitivity of the solution to changes in the resources or equipment available, a number of problems are often solved which differ only in their b-vectors. We shall see that rather than solve each one from the beginning, we can use the solution of one as a starting point for the next. We can save a great many calculations in this way.

Let us suppose, for example, that we wished to solve the bearing-manufacturer problem of Section 4–1, not only with the b-vector used there, let us call it b^1, but also with

$$b^2 = \begin{pmatrix} 10 \\ 12 \\ 13 \end{pmatrix} \quad \text{and} \quad b^3 = \begin{pmatrix} 12 \\ 12 \\ 14 \end{pmatrix}.$$

In Section 4–1, we found the optimal basis to be $B = (A_3, A_4, A_1)$. With b^2 as the constraint vector, the solution relative to this basis is

$$u^B = B^{-1}b^2 = \begin{pmatrix} -4 & -2 & 5 \\ 3 & 1 & -3 \\ 3 & 2 & -4 \end{pmatrix} \begin{pmatrix} 10 \\ 12 \\ 13 \end{pmatrix} = \begin{pmatrix} 1 \\ 3 \\ 2 \end{pmatrix}.$$

Since this u^B is nonnegative, the basis (A_3, A_4, A_1) is *feasible* for the problem. Since the simplex criteria do not depend at all on the b-vector, but only on the basis, they remain all nonpositive. Therefore, the same basis that was optimal for the old vector, b^1, is optimal for the new vector, b^2. We see that, in general, *if the old optimal basis remains **feasible** when the constraint vector is changed, it remains **optimal** as well.*

In the case of b^3, however, the story is quite different, for we find that u^B becomes

$$u^B = B^{-1}b^3 = \begin{pmatrix} -4 & -2 & 5 \\ 3 & 1 & -3 \\ 3 & 2 & -4 \end{pmatrix}\begin{pmatrix} 12 \\ 12 \\ 14 \end{pmatrix} = \begin{pmatrix} -2 \\ 6 \\ 4 \end{pmatrix}.$$

Because of the -2 in u^B, the formerly optimal basis is no longer feasible. Were it feasible, of course, it would still be optimal, for the simplex criteria are all zero or less. Our strategy will be to change the basis so as to keep the simplex criteria nonpositive as we eliminate the negative elements in the solution. (Note the duality to the "primal" simplex method in which we keep the solution nonnegative as we eliminate the positive elements of the simplex criteria row.) Thus, when we reach a feasible solution, it will be optimal. Because bringing into the basis an activity with a negative simplex criterion lowers the objective function (from its infeasible value), no basis can be repeated. After a finite number of iterations, we either find a feasible (and optimal) solution or we discover that the problem has no feasible solution.

We can easily execute this strategy by starting from the final tableau of the full-matrix transformation solution of the original problem. Table 4–9,

Table 4–9

THE DUAL SIMPLEX METHOD

Tableau	Basis	u				$B^{-1}A$			
0	v	-50	0	-2	0	0	-1	-2	-1
	A_3	-2	0	-1	1	0	-4	-2	5
	A_4	6	0	2	0	1	3	1	-3
	A_1	4	1	1	0	0	3	2	-4
1	v	-49.5	0	-1.75	-0.25	0	0	-1.5	-2.5
	A_5	0.5	0	0.25	-0.25	0	1	0.5	-1.25
	A_4	4.5	0	1.25	0.75	1	0	-0.5	0.75
	A_1	2.5	1	0.25	0.75	0	0	0.5	-0.25

therefore, repeats in its first tableau the final tableau of Table 4–4, except for the u-column. In the u-column, we now place $B^{-1}b^3 = (-2, 6, 4)$, instead of $B^{-1}b^1$.

We first choose as an activity to *eliminate* from the basis any one which has a negative coefficient in the u-column. We may as well choose the activity, call it B_r, with the most negative coefficient. In Table 4–9, we select A_3 to be eliminated.

What activity shall we *introduce*? It will help us find the answer to use the notation a_{ij}^B for the elements of $B^{-1}A$ and to call the basis following B in the iterative procedure $(B + 1)$. Now, we want to choose an activity to introduce from among only those A_k such that a_{rk}^B is negative, for if

$$a_{rk}^B > 0, \qquad \text{then} \qquad u_r^{(B+1)} = \frac{u_r^B}{a_{rk}^B} < 0.$$

We would then have introduced A_k at a *negative* level and thereby *increased* the objective function, which we are now trying to reduce to a feasible level. If $a_{rj}^B \geq 0$ for all j, there is no feasible solution to the system. Why? In Table 4–9, we see that activities 2, 5, and 6 meet the $a_{rk}^B < 0$ requirement. From among those which meet this requirement, we wish to choose the one which will ensure that $v^{(B+1)} \leq 0$. If activity k is introduced, then by the pivot rule for the simplex criteria,

$$v_j^{(B+1)} = v_j^B - \frac{v_k^B a_{rj}^B}{a_{rk}^B}, \qquad j = 1, \ldots, m. \qquad (4\text{–}5.1)$$

To keep $v^{(B+1)}$ nonpositive, we therefore need only to choose k so that

$$v_j^B \leq \frac{v_k^B a_{rj}^B}{a_{rk}^B} \qquad \text{over all } j \text{ for which} \quad a_{rj}^B > 0. \qquad (4\text{–}5.2)$$

Dividing both sides of (4–5.2) by a_{rj}^B, which is negative, we get the following simple rule: Choose k so that

$$\frac{v_k^B}{a_{rk}^B} = \min_{[j \,|\, a_{rj}^B < 0]} \left(\frac{v_j^B}{a_{rj}^B} \right). \qquad (4\text{–}5.3)$$

In Table 4–9, this rule selects A_5 to enter the basis. Calculation of the u-column of the next tableau shows that this new basis is feasible; as guaranteed, the simplex criteria are nonpositive, so our feasible solution is also optimal.

The rules of this dual method are easy to remember, because each of them is dual to a rule in the primal method. In the dual method, the activity to be *eliminated* is chosen first by a rule corresponding to the *Introduction* Rule in the primal. Then the activity to be *introduced* is selected by a rule corresponding to the *Elimination* Rule of the primal. The pivot operation is exactly the same in both methods.

There are applications of the dual method to several problems other than the analysis of the sensitivity of the solution to the *b*-vector. It can be used for adding an additional constraint after a problem has been solved. Problem 2 indicates the approach to this problem. The dual method is also valuable in the solution of *mixed integer programming* problems, problems in which some of the variables are required to be either 0 or 1, with nothing in-between allowed. Such integer variables are necessary for the study of problems with indivisibilities or economies of scale. No completely satisfactory scheme has been devised for the solution of such problems. The following method is simpler than most others and has proved rather efficient in practice. It is taken from the Driebeek article in the readings listed for this chapter.

For each integer variable x_i, we introduce the constraints

$$x_i \geq \alpha_i \qquad \text{or} \qquad -x_i \leq -\alpha_i,$$
$$x_i \leq \beta_i.$$

Initially, we put $\beta_i = 1$ and $\alpha_i = 0$ (that is, $0 \leq x_i \leq 1$), and then solve the resulting linear program. We shall call this the "continuous" problem, for it ignores the integer requirements. If, by good luck, the integer variables come out to be all 0 or 1, the problem is solved; but if, as is likely, some integer variable is found in the forbidden interior of the [0, 1] interval, then we must change the values of α_i and β_i so as to pin each integer variable, x_i, either to 0 ($\alpha_i = \beta_i = 0$) or to 1 ($\alpha_i = \beta_i = 1$). We then apply the dual method to find the maximum value for this modified "pinned-variable" problem. If there are n integer variables, there are a total of 2^n different pinned-variable problems to solve, one for each possible set of values for the integer variables. The problem with the highest value of the objective function gives the optimal solution to the integer programming problem.

Fortunately, we do not have to complete the solution of each of these problems, for the computation on any one of them can be stopped if the value of its objective function falls below that of a feasible integer solution obtained on an earlier problem. Moreover, we shall see that it is easy to place a lower bound on the "loss" between the continuous program and the pinned-variable program, that is, on the difference between the maximum value of the objective function for the continuous program and the maximum for the pinned-variable problems. We can then try the pinned-variable problems in the order of increasing bounds on the loss, starting with the one with the smallest "guaranteed" loss. When we find that the guaranteed loss on all subsequent problems is greater than the actual loss on one already tried, we can stop the calculations, for we have already found the answer.

We state here the rules for calculating the lower bounds on the loss in going from the continuous to a pinned-variable problem. The detailed justification makes such a good exercise that we leave it as Problem 3. Let us denote the value of x_i in the continuous solution by $\bar{x}_i$. Two cases must be distinguished.

CASE I. $\bar{x}_i$ *is integer.* If $\bar{x}_i = 1$, then any pinned-variable problem in which $x_i = 0$ has a loss of *at least* π_{β_i}, the simplex multiplier for the β_i restraint. If $\bar{x}_i = 0$, then any solution in which $x_i = 1$ has a loss of at least π_{α_i}, the simplex multiplier for the α_i restraint. Moreover, losses of this type are *additive;* if $\bar{x}_i = 0$ and $\bar{x}_j = 1$, then any solution in which $x_i = 1$ and $x_j = 0$ will have a loss of *at least* $\pi_{\alpha_i} + \pi_{\beta_j}$. (This Case I loss will occur as soon as we substitute the new values of α_i and β_i, that is, before we change the basis. If a change in the basis is also necessary, the loss will be even greater.)

CASE II. $\bar{x}_i$ *is noninteger.* In this case, the slack activities for both the α_i and β_i restraints will be in the basis, and

$$\pi_{\alpha i} = \pi_{\beta i} = 0.$$

But any solution in which $x_i = 0$ (respectively, $x_i = 1$) will incur a loss of *at least*

$$\frac{(\bar{x}_i - 1)v_k^B}{a_{rk}^B},$$

where a_{rk}^B is the pivot element chosen by the rules of the dual simplex method which is to be eliminated from the basis the slack activity for the β_i (respectively, α_i) restraint. (Pinning x_i to 0 gives the slack variable for β_i a negative value, namely $\bar{x}_i - 1$, and the pivot operation to eliminate that activity causes the loss indicated above.) These losses are *not* additive.

The guaranteed loss for any "pinning" of the variables is then the greater of (a) the sum of the Case I losses, and (b) the greatest of the Case II losses associated with that pinning.

Although even the simplest problems of this type run into heavy computations when done by hand, the method has been found quite efficient for machine solution of problems having up to 20 integer variables. Other methods have been developed which are more interesting mathematically, but they have proved less efficient in practice than this relatively simple and direct method. (See the Dantzig book listed in the Suggested Readings.)

PROBLEMS

1. What would be the optimal solution for the bearing manufacturer of the text if he (a) broke a grinder, (b) then broke also a press and a lathe, and (c) got the lathe fixed. [Note how the π's for the three types of machinery can be used to give a lower bound on the loss incurred in going from the previous optimal to each of the three "broken-down" conditions.]

2. Suppose that after a problem has been solved it is realized (probably from looking at the answers) that an additional constraint should have been included. Show how this addition can be accomplished by the dual method. [*Hint:* A basis for the new problem can be made from the optimal basis for the old by the addition of the slack activity for the new constraint.] Show that

   a) the inverse of this basis for the new problem can be quickly calculated from the inverse of the basis of the old,
   b) the simplex criteria for this basis are nonpositive, but
   c) the new basis is not feasible if the added constraint was not already satisfied.

3. Justify in detail the lower bounds on the losses from pinning the variables in the mixed-integer programming problems.

*4–6 DEGENERACY IN LINEAR PROGRAMMING

In this section, we complete the proof of Theorem 4–1 by showing that the simplex method can be modified to assure arrival at $a \leq 0$, even if the use level of the newly introduced activity is not always greater than zero. We needed to assume that t_r was always positive only to assure ourselves that no basis was ever repeated.

This proof uses the concept of a lexicographic ordering of vectors, an ordering, that is, like the order of words in a dictionary. For example, the decreasing lexicographic order of the four vectors

$$(3, 1, 7)$$
$$(2, 8, -7)$$
$$(3, -1, 20)$$
$$(2, 8, 5)$$

is

$$(3, 1, 7)$$
$$(3, -1, 20)$$
$$(2, 8, 5)$$
$$(2, 8, -7).$$

Note that the $-\pi$-rows in Table 4–1 are in lexicographic order, though only the first element of each is used to get this order. We shall show how the simplex method can be augmented to ensure that even when their first elements do not decrease, these vectors steadily progress lexicographically, and thus guarantee that no basis is ever repeated.

The possibility of degeneracy, that is, of having $t_r = 0$, arises only when there is a 0 in the u^B-vector. If the initial u^B-vector is strictly positive, then a 0 can appear only in the tableau *after* the tableau in which the Elimination Rule has resulted in a *tie* for the activity to be eliminated from the basis.

By a proper rule for breaking such ties, the lexicographic decline in the $-\pi$-row can be assured. Suppose that a tie occurs between B_r and B_s, that is,

$$\min_{[i\,|\,p_i>0]} \frac{u_i^B}{p_i} = \frac{u_r^B}{p_r} = \frac{u_s^B}{p_s}, \qquad s \neq r. \tag{4–6.1}$$

Tie-breaking Elimination Rule. To choose the activity to be eliminated from among those tied, select the one having the smallest B_{i1}^{-1}/p_i ratio. If some activities are still tied, choose from among these the one with the smallest B_{i2}^{-1}/p_i ratio. If ties remain, go on to B_{i3}^{-1}/p_i, B_{i4}^{-1}/p_i, etc.

The tie must eventually be broken, for otherwise two rows of the B^{-1} matrix would be proportional to each other, which is impossible in a non-singular matrix such as B^{-1}. Let us suppose that the tie is broken on the first column of B^{-1} and that B_r is the activity chosen to be eliminated, that is,

$$\frac{B_{r1}^{-1}}{p_r} < \frac{B_{s1}^{-1}}{p_s}. \tag{4–6.2}$$

Then p_r will be the pivot element, and after the pivot operation, we will have

$$u_s^{(B+1)} = u_s^B - \frac{u_r^B p_s}{p_r} = 0, \qquad \text{by Eq. (4–6.1)}, \tag{4–6.3}$$

and

$$(B+1)_{s1}^{-1} = B_{s1}^{-1} - \frac{B_{r1}^{-1} p_s}{p_r} > 0, \qquad \text{by Eq. (4–6.2)}. \tag{4–6.4}$$

If B_s is eliminated at the next step of the simplex procedure, the zero value of $u_s^{(B+1)}$ will mean that the value of the objective function will not change in that pivot operation, but the positivity of $(B+1)_{s1}^{-1}$ ensures that this operation *would* decrease the value of $-\pi_1$. (Think through the calculation of the $-\pi$-vector by the pivot operation, and remember that the simplex criterion of the activity being introduced and the pivot element are both positive.) The $-\pi$-row, therefore, decreases lexicographically and assures us that no basis will be repeated.

Were the tie not broken until the jth column of B^{-1} was reached, Eq. (4–6.4) would be replaced by

$$(B + 1)_{sh}^{-1} = B_{sh}^{-1} - \frac{B_{rh}^{-1} p_s}{p_r} = 0, \qquad h = 1, \ldots, j - 1,$$

and

$$(B + 1)_{sj}^{-1} = B_{sj}^{-1} - \frac{B_{rj}^{-1} p_s}{p_r} > 0.$$

Then $-\pi_1, \ldots, -\pi_{j-1}$ would remain unchanged but $-\pi_j$ would decrease to provide the lexicographic order.

Application of the above rule, moreover, assures lexicographic progress of the $(-z, -\pi)$ vector even if some of the initial elements of u^B are zero. This is because *the basic condition required for lexicographic progress—that in any row containing a zero in the u^B-column, the first nonzero element in the B^{-1}-matrix be positive*—is initially satisfied by the E-basis. Any pivot operation in which (a) the p-vector has a positive element in this row will preserve this condition by the tie-breaking rule; (b) the p-vector has a zero in this row will leave the row unchanged; (c) the p-vector has a negative element in this row will either eliminate the zero from the u-column or, if $t_r = 0$, preserve the condition, since then the first nonzero element of the pivot row must be positive.

Thus we can be sure that in no case will any basis ever be repeated. Hence after a finite number of changes, the optimal basis must be reached. We have therefore completed the proof of Theorem 4–1.

CHAPTER 5

NONLINEAR MAXIMIZATION

5-1 THE LAGRANGIAN MULTIPLIER

Thus far, we have dealt only with maximization problems in which both the function to be maximized and the constraints on the variables are linear and the variables are required to be nonnegative. In a number of economic problems, however, either the objective function or the constraints, or both, may be nonlinear, while the nonnegativity of the variables is unimportant, since it will be assured by simply being at a maximum. Such problems are the subject of this and the next two sections. Then in Section 5–4, we shall see the generalization of both approaches in a unified theory.

We shall use two results from calculus with which the reader should be sure he is familiar before proceeding.

1) If the partial derivatives

$$\frac{\partial f}{\partial x_j} = f_j(x_1, \ldots, x_m), \qquad j = 1, \ldots, m$$

of the function $f(x_1, \ldots, x_m)$ exist at the point $x^0 = (x_1^0, \ldots, x_m^0)$, then a necessary condition for $f(x)$ to have a local maximum or minimum at x^0 is that $f_j(x^0) = 0$ for $j = 1, \ldots, m$.

2) *The chain rule.* If $x_i = \varphi^i(u_1, \ldots, u_n)$ and $y = f(x_1, \ldots, x_m)$, then

$$\frac{\partial y}{\partial u_j} = \sum_{i=1}^{m} f_i \varphi_j^i.$$

We may illustrate our problem with the following example.

Example. During the past week, a soap manufacturer has produced 100 tons of soap. He has three distribution warehouses with stocks, as of Friday afternoon, of 225, 300, and 375 tons, respectively. The inventory cost curves of the three warehouses are

$$C_1 = 0.2S_1 - 50 \ln S_1 + 300,$$
$$C_2 = 0.2S_2 - 60 \ln S_2 + 400,$$
$$C_3 = 0.2S_3 - 70 \ln S_3 + 500,$$

where C_i is the weekly cost and S_i is the stock of warehouse i on Monday. (See Fig. 5–1.) The curves rise to the left because of the danger of running out when stocks are low; the rise to the right is because of interest and insurance costs of holding inventories. Shipments made on Friday arrive on Monday. How should the 100 tons production be distributed among the warehouses to minimize the inventory costs?

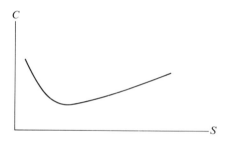

Figure 5–1

If we let x_i be the shipments to the ith warehouse and $\overline{S}_i$ its present stock, then the general cost function for the ith warehouse is

$$C_i = a_i(\overline{S}_i + x_i) - b_i \ln (\overline{S}_i + X_i) + k_i.$$

The problem is then to minimize

$$f(x) = f(x_1, x_2, x_3)$$
$$= \sum_{i=1}^{3} a_i(\overline{S}_i + x_i) - b_i \ln (\overline{S}_i + x_i) + k_i \qquad (5\text{–}1.1)$$

subject to

$$g(x) = g(x_1, x_2, x_3) = x_1 + x_2 + x_3 - 100 = 0. \qquad (5\text{–}1.2)$$

This example is an instance of the following general problem:

Maximize (or minimize) $f(x) = f(x_1, \ldots, x_m)$ (5–1.3)

subject to $g(x) = g(x_1, \ldots, x_m) = 0.$ (5–1.4)

One method of solving the example is to use (5–1.2) to solve for x_1 in terms of x_2 and x_3,

$$x_1 = \varphi(x_2, x_3) = 100 - x_2 - x_3, \qquad (5\text{–}1.5)$$

and then substitute this expression for x_1 into (5–1.1) to express f in terms of x_2 and x_3:

$$f(x_1, x_2, x_3) = f(\varphi(x_2, x_3), x_2, x_3) = F(x_2, x_3) \qquad (5\text{–}1.6)$$

for all x_1, x_2, x_3 *which satisfy* (5–1.2). (The right-hand equality defines the function F.) Lastly, we set

$$\frac{\partial F}{\partial x_2} = 0 \qquad \text{and} \qquad \frac{\partial F}{\partial x_3} = 0,$$

and solve these equations for x_2 and x_3, and then use (5–1.5) to find x_1.

This same approach may be applied to the general problem posed by (5–1.3) and (5–1.4) to obtain an important and useful result. Let $x_1 = \varphi(x_2, \dots, x_m)$ be the solution of (5–1.4) for x_1, that is,

$$g(\varphi(x_2, \dots, x_m), x_2, \dots, x_m) \equiv 0, \qquad (5\text{–}1.7)$$

where the $\equiv$ means "identically equal to," i.e., the equality holds for all values of the variables. Now substitute for x_1 in (5–1.3) to get

$$\begin{aligned} f(x_1, \dots, x_m) &= f(\varphi(x_2, \dots, x_m), x_2, \dots, x_m) \\ &= F(x_2, \dots, x_m) \end{aligned} \qquad (5\text{–}1.8)$$

for all x which satisfy (5–1.4). Now setting equal to zero the partial derivatives of F with respect to $x_2, \dots, x_m$ yields

$$0 = F_i = f_1 \varphi_i + f_i \qquad \text{for} \quad i = 2, \dots, m. \qquad (5\text{–}1.9)$$

The last equality follows from the chain rule. Differentiating (5–1.7) with respect to x_i gives

$$g_1 \varphi_i + g_i = 0, \qquad i = 2, \dots, m, \qquad (5\text{–}1.10)$$

because the derivative of an expression which is identically zero is certainly also identically zero. We can solve (5–1.10) for φ_i,

$$\varphi_i = \frac{-g_i}{g_1}, \qquad i = 2, \dots, m,$$

and substitute this expression into (5–1.9) to obtain

$$f_i - \left(\frac{f_1}{g_1}\right) g_i = 0, \qquad i = 2, \dots, m. \qquad (5\text{–}1.11)$$

If we define λ by

$$\lambda = \frac{f_1}{g_1}, \qquad (5\text{–}1.12)$$

Eqs. (5–1.11) and (5–1.12) may be written simply and symmetrically as

$$f_i - \lambda g_i = 0, \qquad i = 1, \ldots, m. \tag{5–1.13}$$

This λ is called a *Lagrangian multiplier*. It may be thought of as a penalty for violating the constraint, for Eq. (5–1.13) is exactly what we would obtain if we maximized without constraint the following function, called the Lagrangian,

$$L(x_1, \ldots, x_m, \lambda) = f(x_1, \ldots, x_m) - \lambda g(x_1, \ldots, x_m). \tag{5–1.14}$$

In the above example, the Lagrangian function becomes

$$L = \sum_{i=1}^{3} \left(a_i(\bar{S}_i + x_i) - b_i \ln(\bar{S}_i + x_i) + k_i \right) - \lambda \left(\sum_{i=1}^{3} x_i - 100 \right).$$

$$\tag{5–1.15}$$

Minimizing L with respect to x_1, x_2, x_3 and λ gives

$$\frac{\partial L}{\partial x_i} = a_i - \frac{b_i}{\bar{S}_i + x_i} - \lambda = 0, \qquad i = 1, 2, 3, \tag{5–1.16}$$

and

$$\frac{\partial L}{\partial \lambda} = \sum_{i=1}^{3} x_i - 100 = g(x) = 0. \tag{5–1.17}$$

In this instance, the quantity $\sum_{i=1}^{3} x_i - 100$ may be thought of as the negative of the amount not shipped, but stored, at the factory. The Lagrangian multiplier, λ, is then to be thought of as the charge for this factory storage. A value of λ may be chosen and the x_i computed from (5–1.16). If the value of λ is chosen too low, the resulting x_i give $g(x) < 0$, that is, less shipments are called for than there is soap to supply. Since the factory is not in a position either to store soap—room must be made for next week's production—or to ship more than it has made, this factory storage charge must be adjusted to make shipments exactly equal to 100.

By trying a few values of λ, we can quickly solve the above example. It is convenient to rewrite (5–1.16) as

$$x_i = \frac{b_i}{a_i - \lambda} - \bar{S}_i$$

or

$$x_1 = \frac{50}{0.2 - \lambda} - 225, \qquad x_2 = \frac{60}{0.2 - \lambda} - 300, \qquad x_3 = \frac{70}{0.2 - \lambda} - 375.$$

If we choose $\lambda = 0$, we get the figures shown in column 1 of Table 5–1. With this value of λ, there are no net shipments; the whole 100 tons stay at the factory. Clearly, we need a higher value of λ. Let us try $\lambda = 0.05$; the results, column 2 of the table, show that this value is too high. In Fig. 5–2, these two choices of λ are plotted against the resulting values of $g(x)$. A line connecting the two points suggests that a value of $\lambda = 0.02$ should be about right. Column 3 of the table shows the result to be $g(x) = 0$, and the problem is therefore solved with $x_1 = 53$, $x_2 = 33$, $x_3 = 14$.

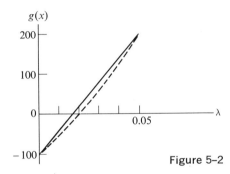

Table 5-1

Column	1	2	3
λ	0	0.05	0.02
x_1	25	109	53
x_2	0	100	33
x_3	-25	91	14
$g(x)$	-100	200	0

Figure 5-2

This example shows the Lagrangian multiplier in one of its typical and most useful roles, that of a "decomposer" or "decentralizer." Suppose the factory manager announced to the warehouse operators that he would give them λ dollars to take a ton of soap off his hands for the week and then asked each operator how much he would take. Each operator, being well schooled in economics, knows that he must maximize his revenue, λx_i, less his costs, $a_i(\bar{S}_i + x_i) - b_i \ln (\bar{S}_i + x_i) + k_i$. This maximization gives Eq. (5–1.16). Thus, if the factory manager announces the right λ, the resulting orders will be feasible and optimal for the system. Moreover, he can, just as we did, keep adjusting λ until the orders from the warehouse satisfy his constraint. Note that by using this process, *he does not need to know the cost functions of the warehouses.* Optimal allocation can be achieved without complete information at the center when the Lagrangian multiplier is used to decentralize decisions.

Since the Lagrangian multiplier is often referred to as a "device," not to say "trick" or "gimmick," we must emphasize that it is *not* something artificially introduced into the maximization problem. We did not put it into the problem; in Eq. (5–1.11), it just naturally emerged from the problem. It is there whether we recognize it or not.

In problems in which there are n restraints, rather than just one as above, a similar argument shows that by proper choice of $\lambda_1, \ldots, \lambda_n$, the constrained maximization problem,

$$\text{maximize} \quad f(x_1, \ldots, x_m) = 0$$
$$\text{subject to} \quad g^1(x_1, \ldots, x_m) = 0,$$
$$g^n(x_1, \ldots, x_m) = 0,$$

can be replaced by the unconstrained problem,

$$\text{maximize} \quad L = f(x_1, \ldots, x_m) - \sum_{j=1}^{n} \lambda_j g^j(x_1, \ldots, x_m) \qquad (5\text{-}1.18)$$

with respect to the x's and the λ's. This approach yields the equations

$$f_i - \sum_{j=1}^{n} \lambda_j g_i^j = 0, \qquad i = 1, \ldots, m. \qquad (5\text{-}1.19)$$

PROBLEMS

1. An electric utility has two generating plants in which the total costs per hour, C_1 and C_2, are

$$C_1 = \$80 + 2x_1 + 0.001x_1^2,$$
$$C_2 = \$90 + 1.5x_2 + 0.002x_2^2,$$

respectively. Here x_1 is the generation by plant i in megawatts. If the utility is required to produce 2000 megawatts in a certain hour, how should it allocate this load between the two plants? Use the Lagrangian method, and interpret the multiplier.

2. An advertiser has found that the amount of weekly sales (in thousands of dollars) of his product which he can get through the various advertising media is determined by the amount spent on these media as follows:

$$\text{television:} \quad S_T = 4T^{0.9},$$
$$\text{radio:} \quad S_R = 6R^{0.8},$$
$$\text{newspaper:} \quad S_N = 10N^{0.7},$$

where T, R, and N are the amounts, in thousands of dollars, spent weekly on the respective media. If the seller has a weekly advertising budget of $100,000, how should it be distributed among the media? How much could he increase sales by spending one more dollar on advertising? (Use logarithms.)

3. A certain industry has a production function $Q = CL^a K^{1-a}$, where Q is value added, L is labor, and K is capital. Show that if the prices of capital and labor are constant and the industry minimizes the cost of producing its output, then the fraction of value added going to labor will be a.

4. A corn farmer finds that his production function is

$$x_1 - (30 + 0.5x_2 + 0.06x_3 - 0.02x_2^2 + 0.001x_2x_3 - 0.001x_3^2) = 0,$$

where x_1 is the yield in bushels per acre and x_2 and x_3 are the pounds of nitrogenous and phosphate fertilizer, respectively, applied per acre. If corn sells for \$1 a bushel and nitrogenous and phosphate fertilizer cost 3 cents and 2 cents a pound, respectively, how much of each fertilizer should be used to maximize profits?

*5-2 DISPLACEMENT OF A MAXIMUM

"How does the solution change when the situation changes?" This question, which is often almost as important as that which asks what the solution is, may be answered very easily for some problems of the sort discussed in the last section. The method is well illustrated in the theory of consumer behavior.

Suppose that a consumer maximizes his utility function

$$u = f(x_1, \ldots, x_m)$$

subject to the budget constraint $\sum_{j=1}^{m} p_j x_j = y$, where y is his income, the p's are prices, and the x's are amounts consumed of various goods. How then do his demands change as some price, say p_1, varies? That is, what is the value of $\partial x_i/\partial p_1$ for $i = 1, \ldots, m$?

The Lagrangian expression for this problem is

$$L = f(x_1, \ldots, x_m) - \lambda \left(\sum_{j=1}^{m} p_j x_j - y \right), \qquad (5\text{-}2.1)$$

and its maximization requires that

$$\frac{\partial L}{\partial x_i} = f_i(x_1, \ldots, x_m) - \lambda p_i = 0, \qquad i = 1, \ldots, m, \qquad (5\text{-}2.2)$$

$$\frac{\partial L}{\partial \lambda} = \sum_{j=1}^{m} p_j x_j - y = 0.$$

In this problem, λ becomes the marginal utility of income or of money. (Why?)

Now Eqs. (5-2.2) must hold at any optimum. As the prices and income vary, the x's *and* λ vary, but the equations still hold. (In economic terms, λ, the marginal utility of money, varies as price changes cause the purchasing power of money to change.) Thus, the x's and λ are functions of the prices and income: for $i = 1, \ldots, m$,

$$x_i = x_i(p_1, \ldots, p_m, y), \qquad \text{and} \qquad \lambda = \lambda(p_1, \ldots, p_m, y).$$

When these demand functions are substituted into (5–2.2), the quantities on the left become *identically* equal to 0 in the p's and y. Therefore, the partial derivative of these quantities with respect to p_1 must certainly be zero:

$$\sum_{j=1}^{m} f_{1j}\frac{\partial x_j}{\partial p} - p_1\frac{\partial \lambda}{\partial p} = \lambda,$$

$$\sum_{j=1}^{m} f_{ij}\frac{\partial x_j}{\partial p_1} - p_i\frac{\partial \lambda}{\partial p_1} = 0, \qquad i = 2, \ldots, m, \qquad (5\text{–}2.3)$$

$$\sum_{j=1}^{m} p_j\frac{\partial x_j}{\partial p_1} = -x_1.$$

In matrix form, these equations are

$$\begin{pmatrix} f_{11} & \cdots & f_{1m} & -p_1 \\ f_{21} & \cdots & f_{2m} & -p_2 \\ \vdots & & \vdots & \vdots \\ f_{m1} & \cdots & f_{mm} & -p_m \\ -p_1 & \cdots & -p_m & 0 \end{pmatrix} \begin{pmatrix} \frac{\partial x_1}{\partial p_1} \\ \frac{\partial x_2}{\partial p_1} \\ \vdots \\ \frac{\partial x_m}{\partial p_1} \\ \frac{\partial \lambda}{\partial p_1} \end{pmatrix} = \begin{pmatrix} \lambda \\ 0 \\ \vdots \\ 0 \\ x_1 \end{pmatrix}. \qquad (5\text{–}2.4)$$

Solving for $\partial x_i/p_1$ gives

$$\frac{\partial x_i}{\partial p_1} = \lambda s_{i1} + s_{i,m+1}x_1, \qquad i = 1, \ldots, m, \qquad (5\text{–}2.5)$$

where the s's are the elements of the inverse of the matrix on the left-hand side of (5–2.4). Similarly, one can show that

$$\frac{\partial x_i}{\partial p_j} = \lambda s_{ij} + s_{i,m+1}x_j, \qquad i = 1, \ldots, m, \quad j = 1, \ldots, m, \qquad (5\text{–}2.6)$$

and

$$\frac{\partial x_i}{\partial y} = -s_{i,m+1}. \qquad (5\text{–}2.7)$$

Because of Eq. (5–2.7), the second term on the right-hand side of Eq. (5–2.6) is called the *income effect* of the price change, and the first term, the *substitution effect*. For a second reason for the name "substitution effect," see Problem 3. Equation (5–2.6) is known as the Slutsky equation.

PROBLEMS

1. In Problem 2 of Section 5–1, let p_1, p_2, and p_3 be the prices of advertising time (or space) in the three media, and let y be the total advertising budget. Assume that initially $p_1 = p_2 = p_3 = 1$, and determine

$$\frac{\partial x_2}{\partial p_1}, \quad \frac{\partial x_2}{\partial p_2}, \quad \frac{\partial x_1}{\partial p_2}, \quad \text{and} \quad \frac{\partial x_2}{\partial y},$$

   all evaluated at the optimum found in the last section.

2. Does the assumption that the consumer's utility function has continuous partial derivatives and that therefore $f_{ij} = f_{ji}$ have any empirical implications?

3. Show that if a consumer minimizes the expenditure required to achieve a *fixed* level of utility, then as prices change, $\partial x_i/\partial p_j = \lambda s_{ij}$. [*Hint:* The Lagrangian $L = \sum x_i p_i - \mu f(x)$ gives $p_i - \mu f_i(x) = 0$, which, when we define $\lambda = 1/\mu$, becomes $f_i(x) - \lambda p_i = 0$, as in (5–2.2).]

4. Write the matrix in Eq. (5–2.4) in partitioned form as

$$\begin{pmatrix} f & -p \\ -p' & 0 \end{pmatrix},$$

   and find its inverse by the rule of Section 1–5. Show that the "substitution effects" are actually made up of two components, one being a sort of second-order income effect, and the other being a "pure" substitution effect. Show further that if $f(x_1, \ldots, x_m)$ is separable, that is, if it can be written

$$f(x_1, \ldots, x_m) = f^1(x_1) + f^2(x_2) + \cdots + f^m(x_m),$$

   then *all* the partial derivatives, $\partial x_i/\partial p_j$ for $i, j = 1, \ldots, m$, can be calculated, provided we know the income effects and *one* of the partial derivatives with respect to price, say, $\partial x_1/\partial p_1$. (An empirical study using this result can be found in L. Johansen's book, *A Multi-Sectoral Model of Economic Growth.* North-Holland Publishing Company, Amsterdam, 1960).

*5–3 SECOND-ORDER NECESSARY CONDITIONS
FOR A CONSTRAINED MAXIMUM

This section presents the second-order maximum conditions which have played a prominent role in economic theory, though their use in empirical work has been slight. Theorem 5–3 brings out the application of these second-order conditions to the solution of equation systems such as (5–2.4) and thereby to economic theory.

In the following discussion, the letters x and h without subscripts denote m-dimensional vectors or points. We shall be concerned with functions of these m variables and shall usually write simply $f(x)$ in place of $f(x_1, \ldots, x_m)$. We shall also use the notation $\|x\| = \sqrt{x'x}$.

We shall use the following definition of a maximum:

Let $f(x)$ be defined throughout a region containing the point x^0 in its interior. If there is an $\epsilon > 0$ such that $f(x) - f(x^0) \leq 0$ if $\|x - x^0\| < \epsilon$, then $f(x)$ is said to have a maximum at x^0.

Theorem 5-1 (*Necessary conditions for a maximum*). Suppose that all the first and second partial derivatives of $f(x), f_i(x)$ and $f_{ij}(x)$ exist and are continuous throughout a region containing x^0 in its interior. If $f(x)$ has a maximum at x^0, then

i) $\qquad\qquad f_i(x^0) = 0 \qquad$ for $\quad i = 1, \ldots, m$,

ii) $\qquad \displaystyle\sum_{i=1}^{m} \sum_{j=1}^{m} f_{ij}(x^0)h_i h_j = h'Fh \leq 0 \qquad$ for all vectors h.

Here F is the matrix of the f_{ij}.

Proof. Pick any h and define

$$ g(t) = f(x^0 + th), \qquad \text{where } t \text{ is a scalar.} $$

If $f(x)$ has a maximum at x^0, then $g(t)$ must have one at $t = 0$. This $g(t)$ is a function of one variable and has continuous first and second derivatives. Hence, for $g(t)$ to have a maximum at $t = 0$, we must have

$$ g'(0) = \sum_{i=1}^{m} h_i f_i(x) = 0, $$

$$ g''(0) = \sum_{i=1}^{m} \sum_{j=1}^{m} f_{ij}(x)h_i h_j = h'Fh \leq 0. $$

[These expressions for the derivatives of $g(t)$ are found, of course, by application of the chain rule to the definition of $g(t)$.] Since the initial choice of h is arbitrary, the first of the above expressions implies that (i) must hold, and the second implies that (ii) must hold. Q.E.D.

A matrix, such as F, which satisfies the inequality $x'Ax < 0$ for all x not equal to zero is said to be *negative definite*. Necessary and sufficient conditions for a matrix to be negative definite are given in Problem 4 of this section.

Turning now to constrained maxima, we start from the following definition.

Let $f(x)$ and $g(x)$ be defined throughout a region containing the point x^0 in its interior. If $g(x^0) = 0$, and if there is an $\epsilon > 0$ such that $f(x) - f(x^0) \leq 0$ if $\|x - x^0\| < \epsilon$ and $g(x) = 0$, then $f(x)$ is said to have a maximum at x^0 subject to the constraint $g(x) = 0$.

Theorem 5–2 (*Necessary conditions for a constrained maximum*). Suppose that all the first and second partial derivatives of $f(x)$ and $g(x)$ exist and are continuous in a region containing x^0 in its interior. Suppose further that $g(x^0) = 0$ and that $g_i(x^0) \neq 0$ for some i ($i = 1, \ldots, m$). Then necessary conditions for $f(x)$ to have a maximum at x^0 subject to the constraint $g(x) = 0$ are that there exists a number, λ, such that

i) $f_i(x^0) - \lambda g_i(x^0) = 0$ for $i = 1, \ldots, m,$

ii) $\displaystyle\sum_{i=1}^{m}\sum_{j=1}^{m} [f_{ij}(x^0) - \lambda g_{ij}(x^0)]h_i h_j \leq 0$ for all h such that

$$\sum_{i=1}^{m} g_i(x^0)h_i = 0.$$

Note that condition (i) was established in Section 5–1; we therefore begin the proof by paralleling the discussion there.

Proof. Suppose, for convenience, that $g_m(x^0) \neq 0$. That fact is sufficient to guarantee (by the implicit function theorem) that there exists a function $x_m = \varphi(x_1, \ldots, x_{m-1})$ possessing the first partial derivatives and such that

$$G(x_1, \ldots, x_{m-1}) = g(x_1, \ldots, x_{m-1}, \varphi(x_1, \ldots, x_{m-1})) \equiv 0$$

in some region containing $(x_1^0, \ldots, x_{m-1}^0)$ in its interior. Define

$$F(x_1, \ldots, x_{m-1}) = f(x_1, \ldots, x_{m-1}, \varphi(x_1, \ldots, x_{m-1})).$$

It is then a necessary (and sufficient) condition for $f(x)$ to be a maximum at x^0 subject to $g(x) = 0$ that $F(x_1, \ldots, x_{m-1})$ be an unconstrained maximum at $(x_1^0, \ldots, x_{m-1}^0)$. For there is a neighborhood of $(x_1^0, \ldots, x_{m-1}^0)$ and a corresponding neighborhood of x^0 such that the values assumed by F in the first neighborhood are exactly the values assumed by f at those points of the second neighborhood which satisfy the constraint $g(x) = 0$. To get the results we are looking for, we then have only to write the conditions for unconstrained maxima of F and translate them into terms of f and g.

By Theorem 5–1, necessary conditions for $F(x_1, \ldots, x_{m-1})$ to have an unconstrained maximum at $(x_1^0, \ldots, x_{m-1}^0)$ are that

$$F_i^0 = 0 \quad \text{for} \quad i = 1, \ldots, m-1, \tag{5-3.1}$$

$$\sum_{i=1}^{m-1}\sum_{j=1}^{m-1} F_{ij}^0 h_i h_j \leq 0 \quad \text{for all } h. \tag{5-3.2}$$

(A ^{0} indicates evaluation at x^0.) Now

$$F_i = f_i + f_m \varphi_i \quad \text{and} \quad G_i = g_i + g_m \varphi_i \equiv 0.$$

Hence $\varphi_i = -g_i/g_m$, and (5–3.1) becomes

$$F_i^0 = f_i^0 - (f_m^0/g_m^0)g_i^0 = 0 \quad \text{for} \quad i = 1, \ldots, m-1.$$

By defining $\lambda = (f_m/g_m)$, we have shown the necessity of condition (i). We next apply similar tactics to (5–3.2) and write

$$F_{ij} = f_{ij} + f_{im}\varphi_j + f_{mj}\varphi_i + f_{mm}\varphi_i\varphi_j + f_m\varphi_{ij}, \qquad (5\text{–}3.3)$$

$$G_{ij} = g_{ij} + g_{im}\varphi_j + g_{mj}\varphi_i + g_{mm}\varphi_i\varphi_j + g_m\varphi_{ij} \equiv 0. \qquad (5\text{–}3.4)$$

(The existence of φ_{ij} follows from the fact that $\varphi_i = -g_i/g_m$, $g_m \neq 0$, and g_{ij} and g_{mj} both exist.) Now we see that by multiplying (5–3.4) by λ and subtracting it from (5–3.3), we can eliminate the term involving φ_{ij}. Substitution of the resulting expression into (5–3.2) gives

$$\sum_{i=1}^{m-1}\sum_{j=1}^{m-1} F_{ij}h_ih_j = \sum_{i=1}^{m-1}\sum_{j=1}^{m-1} (f_{ij} - \lambda g_{ij})h_ih_j$$

$$+ \sum_{i=1}^{m-1} (f_{im} - \lambda g_{im})h_i \sum_{j=1}^{m-1} \varphi_j h_j$$

$$+ \sum_{j=1}^{m-1} (f_{mj} - \lambda g_{mj})h_j \sum_{i=1}^{m-1} \varphi_i h_i$$

$$+ (f_{mm} - \lambda g_{mm}) \sum_{j=1}^{m-1} \varphi_j h_j \sum_{i=1}^{m-1} \varphi_i h_i \le 0. \qquad (5\text{–}3.5)$$

It is now only natural to name the quantity $\sum_{i=1}^{m-1} \varphi_i h_i$ which keeps appearing above, and clearly the best name for it is h_m. Then (5–3.5) becomes simply

$$\sum_{i=1}^{m-1}\sum_{j=1}^{m-1} F_{ij}h_ih_j = \sum_{i=1}^{m}\sum_{j=1}^{m} (f_{ij} - \lambda g_{ij})h_ih_j \le 0 \qquad (5\text{–}3.6)$$

for all vectors h such that $h_m = \sum_{i=1}^{m-1} \varphi_i h_i$. Substituting $\varphi_i = g_i/g_m$ makes this condition on h become $\sum_{i=1}^{m} g_i h_i = 0$. The necessity of conditions (i) and (ii) is now established. Q.E.D.

It is clear that we established the necessity of the familiar condition (i) without using the assumptions about the existence and continuity of the second partials of $f(x)$ and $g(x)$.

Condition (ii) of Theorem 5–2 may be written in matrix form as

$$h'Qh \leq 0 \qquad \text{when} \quad bh = 0,$$

where Q is a square m-by-m matrix with elements $q_{ij} = f_{ij}(x^0) - \lambda g_{ij}(x^0)$, and b is a row vector with $b_i = g_i(x^0)$. In this notation, the matrix on the left-hand side of Eq. (5–2.4) is

$$\begin{pmatrix} Q & b' \\ b & 0 \end{pmatrix}.$$

Condition (ii) implies that the first m diagonal elements of the inverse of this matrix are negative or zero. More precisely, it implies the following theorem.

Theorem 5–3. If $h'Qh \leq 0$ for all h such that $bh = 0$, and if

$$\begin{pmatrix} Q & b' \\ b & 0 \end{pmatrix} \begin{pmatrix} h \\ k \end{pmatrix} = e_i \qquad\qquad (5\text{--}3.7)$$

has a solution for any i between 1 and m, then $h_i \leq 0$ in this solution.

Proof. Multiplying both sides of (5–3.7) by (h', k') gives

$$(h', k') \begin{pmatrix} Q & b' \\ b & 0 \end{pmatrix} \begin{pmatrix} h \\ k \end{pmatrix} = (h', k') \begin{pmatrix} Qh + b'k \\ bh \end{pmatrix} = h'Qh + h'b'k + k'bh = h_i.$$

$$(5\text{--}3.8)$$

Since by the last equation of (5–3.7), $bh = 0$, Eq. (5–3.8) becomes $h_i = h'Qh$. But since $bh = 0$, $h'Qh \leq 0$, so $h_i \leq 0$.   Q.E.D.

Applied to Eqs. (5–2.4), this theorem shows that in Eq. (5–2.6), we will have $s_{ii} \leq 0$. Thus the "price" or "substitution" effect, λs_{ii}, will always be negative or zero, since λ is certainly positive.

PROBLEMS

1. A competitive firm has a production function given by $g(x_1, \ldots, x_m) = 0$, where the x's are the amounts produced or used of various goods, the outputs being measured in the positive direction and the inputs, in the negative direction. Use Theorems 5–2 and 5–3 to show that if the firm maximizes its profits, $\pi = \sum p_i x_i$, where the p's are prices, then $\partial x_i/\partial p_i \geq 0$, that is, if the price of an output (input) increases, the amount produced (used) will increase (decrease).

2. Show that if $x'Ax < 0$ for all $x \neq 0$, then $x_i < 0$ in the solution of $Ax = e_i$. (A matrix such as this A is said to be negative definite.)

3. Prove Theorem 5–2 for the case of n constraints. Note that Theorem 5–3 is really already proved for this case, for no use has been made of the fact that b had only one row.

4. If a matrix $-A$ is negative definite, then A is positive definite, that is, $x'Ax > 0$ for all $x \neq 0$. Show that a necessary and sufficient condition for a symmetric matrix A to be positive definite is that all of the pivot elements in the Gauss-Jordan inversion of A be positive.

Suggestion: Partition A and x in the following fashion:

$$\begin{pmatrix} a_{11} & A_{12} \\ A_{21} & A_{22} \end{pmatrix} \quad \text{and} \quad \begin{pmatrix} x_1 \\ x_2 \end{pmatrix},$$

where, if A is n by n, a_{11} and x_1 are 1 by 1 and A_{21} and x_2 are $(n-1)$ by 1. Show that if $a_{11} > 0$ and u_1 is defined by $u_1 = \sqrt{a_{11}}x_1 + (A_{12}/\sqrt{a_{11}})x_2$, then $x'Ax = u_1^2 + x_2'A^{22}x_2$, where $A^{22} = A_{22} - A_{21}A_{12}/a_{11}$ is the matrix in the A_{22}-position after pivoting has been performed on a_{11} in the inversion of the A-matrix. Argue that if all the pivot elements of A are positive, we can find variables $u_1, \ldots, u_n$ such that $x'Ax = \sum_{i=1}^{n} u_i^2$, but that if some of the pivot elements are negative, $x'Ax = \sum_{i=1}^{n} \pm u_i^2$, with exactly as many $+$ signs as there are positive pivot elements. State explicitly the definition of u_1 when a_{11} is negative. (The results of this problem have often been expressed in terms of determinants. After reading the appendix on determinants, you will clearly see how they may be used for this purpose and why nothing is to be gained by their use.)

5–4 THE KUHN-TUCKER THEOREM
OF NONLINEAR PROGRAMMING

The reader has probably sensed a kinship between the simplex multipliers or shadow prices of Section 4–2 and the Lagrangian multipliers of Section 5–1. Both are charges for the use of resources making the resources "worth just what they cost." So that the reader may clearly see the unity of these two concepts, this section presents a general theorem of which both the Lagrangian multiplier and the simplex multipliers are special cases. As in the Lagrangian case, the functions do not have to be linear; but as in the linear programming case, the constraints may be inequalities and the variables are required to be nonnegative.

Let us denote the objective function by $F(x) = F(x_1, \ldots, x_m)$, and let us assume that all its first partial derivatives exist and are continuous in a neighborhood of the point x^0. Furthermore, suppose that the constraints are $G(x) \leq 0$, where $G(x)$ is a vector of functions

$$G(x) = \begin{pmatrix} g^1(x_1, \ldots, x_m) \\ \vdots \\ g^n(x_1, \ldots, x_m) \end{pmatrix},$$

and all the g^i-functions have continuous first partial derivatives at x^0. We shall use the notation

$$G^0 = \begin{pmatrix} g_1^1(x^0) & \cdots & g_m^1(x^0) \\ \vdots & & \vdots \\ g_1^n(x^0) & \cdots & g_m^n(x^0) \end{pmatrix} \quad \text{and} \quad F^0 = \big(F_1(x^0), \ldots, F_m(x^0)\big).$$

One further qualification, however, must be placed on the constraints $G(x)$. In effect, this qualification says that any line starting on the boundary of the feasible set and pointing into or being tangent to the feasible set of each of the $g^i(x) \leq 0$ constraints *individually* must point into or be tangent to the *mutually* feasible set. No constraint may sneak up tangent to the blind side of another constraint. More formally, we may state the qualifications as follows:

Constraint Qualifications. Let x^0 be a (column) vector satisfying $G(x^0) \leq 0, Ix \geq 0$, and let these inequalities be separated into two groups, the tight and the loose, as follows:

$$G_1(x^0) = 0, \quad I_1 x^0 = 0 \quad \text{and} \quad G_2(x^0) < 0, \quad I_2 x^0 > 0.$$

We will consider only the $G(x)$ such that if a vector Δx satisfies

$$G_1^0 \Delta x \leq 0 \quad \text{and} \quad I_1 \Delta x > 0, \tag{5-4.1}$$

then for any $\epsilon > 0$, there exists a vector $\overline{\Delta x}$ which differs from Δx by less than ϵ in all components and which makes $G(x^0 + \delta \overline{\Delta x}) \leq 0$ for all sufficiently small δ.

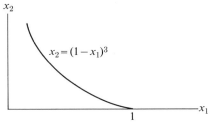

Figure 5-3

This qualification eliminates $G(x)$ with cusps of the sort possessed by the area defined by $x_2 - (1 - x_1)^3 \leq 0, x_1 \geq 0, x_2 \geq 0$ at the point $x_1 = 1, x_2 = 0$. See Fig. 5-3. At that point, there is no $\overline{\Delta x}$ corresponding to $\Delta x = (1, 0)$, because one constraint is tangent to the other. At such a point, derivatives cannot be trusted to tell us the location of the feasible region.

The Kuhn-Tucker Theorem. If x^0 gives a maximum to $F(x)$ subject to the constraints that $G(x) \leq 0, x \geq 0$, where $G(x)$ satisfies the constraint qualification, then there exists a (row) vector $\lambda \geq 0$ such that

i) $F^0 - \lambda G^0 \leq 0$,

ii) $(F^0 - \lambda G^0)x^0 = 0$,

iii) $\lambda G(x^0) = 0$.

Proof. The proof is based on the similar theorem for the linear case, Theorem 4-1 of Section 4-2. Now $F^0 \Delta x \leq 0$ for all Δx satisfying (5-4.1), for suppose, to the contrary, that there exists a Δx such that $F^0 \Delta x > 0$, while $G_1^0 \Delta x \leq 0$ and $I_1 \Delta x_1 \geq 0$. Then by the constraint qualification, there exists a vector $\overline{\Delta x}$ which differs from Δx so little that $F^0 \overline{\Delta x}$ remains positive, but which makes $x^0 + \delta \overline{\Delta x}$ feasible for all sufficiently small $\delta > 0$. By the mean value theorem,

$$F(x^0 + \delta \overline{\Delta x}) - F(x^0) = \sum_{i=1}^{m} F_i(x^0 + \theta \delta \overline{\Delta x}) \overline{\Delta x}_i,$$

where $0 < \theta < 1$. But because $F^0 \overline{\Delta x} > 0$ and F has continuous partial derivatives, the expression on the right will be positive for all sufficiently small δ. Therefore, we can make δ small enough that $F(x^0 + \delta \overline{\Delta x}) \geq F(x^0)$ *and* $x^0 + \delta \overline{\Delta x}$ *is feasible,* contrary to the fact that x^0 gives a maximum value to $F(x)$ subject to the constraints. This contradiction establishes that the solution of the problem

$$\begin{array}{ll} \text{maximize} & F^0 \Delta x \\ \text{subject to} & G_1^0 \Delta x \leq 0, \qquad I_1 \Delta x > 0 \end{array} \qquad (5\text{-}4.2)$$

is, indeed, $\Delta x = 0$. This problem is not quite a linear programming problem, for it does not specify "$\Delta x \geq 0$." In order to apply Theorem 4-1 to the problem, however, we can convert (5-4.2) into a linear programming problem by introducing two new vectors, Δx^+ and Δx^-, such that

$$\Delta x = \Delta x^+ + \Delta x^-, \qquad \Delta x^+ \geq 0, \quad \text{and} \quad \Delta x^- \geq 0.$$

Equation (5-4.2) then becomes the linear programming problem

$$\begin{array}{ll} \text{maximize} & F^0 \Delta x^+ - F^0 \Delta x^- \\ \text{subject to} & G_1^0 \Delta x^+ - G_1^0 \Delta x^- \leq 0, \\ & -I_1 \Delta x^+ + I_1 \Delta x^- \leq 0, \\ & \Delta x^+ \geq 0, \qquad \Delta x^- \geq 0, \end{array} \qquad (5\text{-}4.3)$$

and we obtain the maximum for this problem by setting $\Delta x^+ = \Delta x^- = 0$. Theorem 4-1 now applies to this problem to assure us that there exists a (row) vector $\pi^1 \geq 0$ such that

$$F^0 - \pi^1 \begin{pmatrix} G_1^0 \\ -I_1 \end{pmatrix} \leq 0 \qquad \text{and} \qquad -F^0 - \pi^1 \begin{pmatrix} -G_1^0 \\ I_1 \end{pmatrix} \leq 0.$$

Therefore,

$$F^0 = \pi^1 \begin{pmatrix} G_1^0 \\ -I_1 \end{pmatrix}.$$

We may expand this equation to

$$F^0 = \pi \begin{pmatrix} G^0 \\ -I \end{pmatrix} \tag{5-4.4}$$

by spreading π^1 out into π by inserting a 0 for each row of G_2^0 or I_2 in G or I. By defining λ and μ by $(\lambda, \mu) = \pi$ with λ having n elements and μ having m elements, (5-4.4) may be written as

$$F^0 = \lambda G^0 - \mu \qquad \text{or} \qquad F^0 - \lambda G^0 = -\mu \leq 0, \tag{5-4.5}$$

which is condition (i) of the theorem.

Condition (ii) follows from the fact that if x_i^0 is *not* zero, then the ith row of I is not in I_1, so μ_i is one of the zeros inserted to obtain π from π^1; hence, by (5-4.5) the ith element of $(F^0 - \lambda G^0)$ *is* zero. Therefore

$$(F^0 - \lambda G^0)x^0 = 0.$$

Condition (iii) follows similarly. If $g^i(x^0) \neq 0$, then G_1 does not contain the ith row of G^0, so λ_i is an inserted zero. Hence $\lambda G(x^0) = 0$.   Q.E.D.

PROBLEMS

1. Derive the Lagrangian equations (Eq. 5-1.19) from the Kuhn-Tucker conditions. [*Suggestion:* Consider that the origins for the variables have been so chosen that $x^0 \geq 0$.]

2. Interpret the Kuhn-Tucker conditions in the manner in which the similar linear programming conditions were interpreted.

3. Show that if instead of the constraint $G(x) \leq 0$, we had $G(x) = 0$, the Kuhn-Tucker theorem would still hold, except that we could not guarantee $\pi \geq 0$.

*5-5 MAXIMIZATION IN DYNAMIC PROCESSES.
THE MAXIMUM PRINCIPLE

In this section, we develop a further application of the Kuhn-Tucker theorem which shows how the Lagrangian multipliers enable us to take advantage of the chainlike structure of the constraints which frequently occurs in problems of maximization in dynamic processes. Such problems often have the following form:

$$\text{Maximize} \qquad \sum_{\tau=1}^{T} g^0(x_\tau, u_\tau, \tau)\,\Delta t \qquad (5\text{-}5.1)$$

$$\text{subject to} \qquad x^i_{t+1} - x^i_t = g^i(x_t, u_t, t)\,\Delta t, \qquad (5\text{-}5.2)$$

$$\text{where} \qquad i = 1, \ldots, n, \quad t = 1, \ldots, T-1,$$

$$u_t \geq 0, \quad \text{and} \quad x_0 = a, \text{ a known vector.}$$

Here, x is a vector of n elements, u is a vector of m elements, Δt is the period of time, and T is the horizon or terminal date of the program. An x or u with a single subscript t denotes an entire vector at time t; elements of such a vector are indicated by a superscript on the x.

Note the simple structure of the constraints. The value of x_t is connected directly to only x_{t-1} and x_{t+1}. Of course, the constraints "chain" together to connect all the x_t. The theory we develop in this section exploits this chainlike structure of the constraints to show a useful and similar chain in the Lagrangian multipliers. Before going into the theory, however, we give an economic example to help the reader understand the nature of the problem.

Example. Many firms use inventories of their finished products to insulate their production rate from fluctuations in the sales rate, for fluctuations in production can be more costly than the inventory surpluses or shortages necessary to prevent them. On the other hand, the production rate cannot be totally insensitive to sales, and the problem is to find the optimal balance between fluctuating production and disproportionate inventories. Let v_t be the inventories at the beginning of period t; let s_t and p_t be the sales and production rates, respectively, during that period; and let w_t be the rate of change of the production rate between periods t and $t+1$. We may assume that values of w outside the interval $[-1, 1]$ are simply not feasible. Therefore, letting $w = u - 1$, we have

$$v_{t+1} - v_t = (p_t - s_t)\,\Delta t, \qquad (5\text{-}5.3)$$

$$p_{t+1} - p_t = (u_t - 1)\,\Delta t, \qquad 0 \leq u_t \leq 2. \qquad (5\text{-}5.4)$$

The simplest sort of objective function is

$$z = \sum_{t=1}^{T} [(v_t - a + bs_t)^2 + c(u_t - 1)^2], \qquad (5\text{-}5.5)$$

where $a + bs_t$ represents the lowest-cost inventory when sales are at the level s_t. At lower levels of inventory, the costs of shortages more than outweigh the savings in carrying costs, while at higher levels, the increase in carrying costs outweighs the reduction in shortage costs. The $c(u_t - 1)^2$-term represents the cost of changes in the rate of production. This problem is readily seen to be of the form of (5-5.1) and (5-5.2), except that we have here the additional constraint $u \leq 2$, which will not, however, involve additional computations.

Note that, though there exist necessary connections among the x's of various periods, the u's of each period can be independently chosen. The u is like the position of the accelerator in a car, while the x corresponds to its speed. It is therefore natural to call the u's "control," "instrument," or "policy" variables, and the x's "state" variables.

We now leave our example to return when we have developed the general theory needed to handle it. Our results will be more symmetric if we introduce a new variable, x_t^0, defined by $x_0^0 = 0$ and

$$x_{t+1}^0 - x_t^0 = g^0(x_t, u_t, t)\, \Delta t.$$

This x_t^0 is therefore the "welfare" which has accumulated up to the beginning of period t. Using it, we can write (5-5.1) as

$$\text{maximize} \qquad x_{T+}^0 = g_T^0(x_T, u_T, T) + x_T^0. \qquad (5\text{-}5.1')^*$$

We now form the Lagrangian expression,

$$L = g^0(x_T, u_T, T) + x_T^0 + \sum_{\tau=1}^{T-1} \sum_{j=0}^{n} \lambda_\tau^j (x_{\tau+1}^j - x_\tau^j - g^j(x_\tau, u_\tau, \tau)\, \Delta t).$$

$$(5\text{-}5.6)$$

From the Kuhn-Tucker theorem, we have the following necessary conditions for optimality: from $\partial L/\partial x_t^i = 0$,

$$\lambda_t^i - \lambda_{t-1}^i = - \sum_{j=0}^{n} \lambda_t^j g_{x^i}^j(x_t, u_t, t)\, \Delta t$$

$$\text{for} \quad i = 0, \ldots, n, \quad t = 1, \ldots, T-1; \qquad (5\text{-}5.7)$$

from $\partial L/\partial \lambda_t^i = 0$,

$$x_{t+1}^i - x_t^i = g^i(x_t, u_t, t)\, \Delta t \qquad \text{for} \quad i = 0, \ldots, n; \qquad (5\text{-}5.8)$$

---

* The expressions (5-5.1') and (5-5.1) are identical if $\Delta t = 1$. Had we written "maximize $g^0(x_T, u_T, T)\, \Delta t + x_T^0$," they would have been identical. The span over which we maximize would shrink when we let Δt go to 0, as we shall do in the sequel, and our formulas would become more complicated.

from $\partial L/\partial u_t^i = 0$ or $u_t^i = 0$,

$$\sum_{j=0}^{n} \lambda_t^j g_{u^i}^j(x_t, u_t, t) = 0 \qquad \text{or} \qquad u_t^i = 0$$

$$\text{for} \quad t = 1, \ldots, T-1, \quad i = 1, \ldots, m, \qquad (5\text{-}5.9)$$

$$g_{u^i}^0(x_T, u_T, T) = 0;$$

and from $\partial L/\partial x_T^i = 0$,

$$\lambda_{T-1}^0 = -1,$$

$$\lambda_{T-1}^i = -g_{x^i}^0(x_T, u_T, T) \qquad \text{for} \quad i = 1, \ldots, n. \qquad (5\text{-}5.10)$$

Note from (5–5.7) that λ_t^0 is a constant, since x^0 does not enter any of the g-functions.

If we now take a course of the policy variable, u_t, $t = 1, \ldots, T$ (which for short, we will call a "policy"), we can quickly check to see whether it is optimal. From (5–5.8) we calculate the course of x which is implied by the equation; from (5–5.10) we find the implied values of λ_{T-1}; then, by (5–5.7), we calculate the values of λ back to λ_1. Then, to see whether we have an optimum, we check whether (5–5.9) is satisfied.

We can also express Eq. (5–5.9) by saying "$\sum_{j=0}^{n} \lambda_t^j g^j(x_t, u_t, t)$ is maximum over admissible values of u." This formulation remains valid when the u-vector is subject to upper-bound as well as lower-bound constraints. The detailed derivation of this fact is left as an exercise.

If the division of time into units of length Δt has been simply for the convenience of having a finite number of periods to work with, we will be interested in what happens to Eqs. (5–5.7) through (5–5.10) as Δt goes to 0. In the limit, these equations then become

$$\frac{d\lambda^i}{dt}(t) = -\sum_{j=0}^{n} \lambda^j(t) g_{x^i}^j(x(t), u(t), t), \qquad i = 0, \ldots, n, \qquad (5\text{-}5.7')$$

$$\frac{dx^i}{dt}(t) = g^i(x(t), u(t), t), \qquad (5\text{-}5.8')$$

$$\sum_{j=0}^{n} \lambda^j(t) g^j(x_t, u_t, t) \quad \text{is a maximum over } u, \qquad (5\text{-}5.9')$$

$$\lambda_T^0 = -1,$$

$$\lambda_T^i = -g_{x^i}^0(x_T, u_T, T), \qquad i = 1, \ldots, n. \qquad (5\text{-}5.10')$$

We can write these equations in a compact and useful form by introducing the *Hamiltonian* function

$$H(x, u, t) = \sum_{i=0}^{n} \lambda_i g^i(x, u, t). \qquad (5\text{-}5.11)$$

Then, (5–5.7′) through (5–5.10′) become

$$\frac{d\lambda^i}{dt} = -\frac{\partial H}{\partial x^i},\qquad\qquad\text{(5–5.12)}$$

$$\frac{dx^i}{dt} = \frac{\partial H}{\partial \lambda^i},\qquad\qquad\text{(5–5.13)}$$

and

$H(x, u, t)$ is maximum over admissible u.

In this form, these equations have become known as the *maximum principle*, because of the last conditions. (See the book by Pontryagin in the Suggested Readings.) We must point out that we have not given a completely rigorous derivation of these differential equations, for we have not shown that the limit of the solutions of (5–5.7) through (5–5.10) is a solution of (5–5.7′) through (5–5.10′), nor, indeed, have we proved that a solution of the latter equations will always exist. In most economic problems, it will be obvious that the limiting process is valid.

This differential-equation formulation is valuable in allowing us to deduce the structure of the solution to certain problems, as we shall illustrate at the end of this section. For calculating numerical solutions, we can approximate (5–5.7′) by

$$\lambda_{t+1}^i - \lambda_t^i \approx - \sum_{j=0}^{n} \lambda_t^j g_{x^i}^j(x_t, u_t, t).\qquad\qquad\text{(5–5.7″)}$$

[Note the difference between the left-hand side of (5–5.7), which is exact, and the left-hand side of (5–5.7″), which is an approximation.] Then, if we choose a value of λ_0, we can calculate u_0 by (5–5.9), x_1 by (5–5.8) and λ_1 by (5–5.7). We then repeat the sequence to get u_1, x_2, λ_2, and so on, up to T. At T, we have to check to see whether (5–5.10) is satisfied. If it is not, we then have to go back and try another λ_0. Although a certain amount of searching for λ_0 remains, our theory has greatly reduced the dimension of the space in which we have to search, from Tm values of u_{it} to n values λ_1. Various methods of systematic search may, of course, be employed, but it is not our purpose to go into them here. We may note, however, that if g^i, $i = 1, \ldots, n$, are linear functions, g^0 is quadratic, and there is no danger that a u_{it} will be 0, then Eqs. (5–5.7′) and (5–5.8′) are linear equations in x and λ. Therefore, λ_T and x_T will be linear functions of λ_0:

$$\lambda_T = A\lambda_0 + a,\qquad x_T = B\lambda_0 + b,\qquad \text{and}\qquad u_T = C\lambda_0 + c.$$

Choosing n trial values of λ_0 and computing the resulting λ_T, x_T, and u_T will allow us to determine the A-, B-, and C-matrices and the a-, b-, and *c*-vectors. Substitution of these expressions into (5–5.10) allows us to solve for λ_0.

A problem closely related to the type which we have been discussing is that derived by the addition of the requirement $x_T = b$ to the constraints given in Eq. (5–5.2). To the Lagrangian expression (5–5.6), we should then have to add the term

$$\sum_{i=1}^{n} \mu^i (x_T^i - b_i).$$

Equations (5–5.7) through (5–5.9) would not be affected, but (5–5.10) would become

$$\lambda_T^i = -g_{x^i}^0(x_T, u_T, T) - \mu^i. \tag{5–5.10''}$$

This equation enables us to look at Eqs. (5–5.7′) through (5–5.9′) in a new light. The two boundary conditions $x_0 = a$ and $x_T = b$ together generally determine a unique solution of this system of equations, that is, there is only one λ_0 which will make $x_T = b$. Equation (5–5.10′) then simply serves to determine the μ_i. We thus see that

> *any solution of (5–5.7′) through (5–5.9′) is an optimal way of going from the initial point x_0 to whatever terminal point, x_T, that solution may have.*

We cannot get from the one point to the other in the time allowed in such a way as to obtain a higher value of the objective functions. We express this fact by saying that all solutions of Eqs. (5–5.7′) through (5–5.9′) are *extremal* paths.

Still another variant of our basic problem is that of minimizing the *time* required to go from an initial position, $x = a$, to a specified terminal condition, $x = b$, subject, of course, to the constraints given in Eq. (5–5.2). For this problem, it is a useful preliminary to observe at this point that the derivative of H in Eq. (5–5.11) with respect to t is (a dot over a letter indicates the derivative of the quantity with respect to t):

$$\frac{dH}{dt} = \sum_{j=0}^{n} \dot\lambda^j g^j + \sum_{i=0}^{n} \lambda_i \left[\sum_{j=0}^{n} g_{x^j}^i \dot x^j + \sum_{j=0}^{m} g_{u^j}^i \dot u^j + g_t^i \right].$$

Substituting for $\dot\lambda$ and $\dot x$ from (5–5.7′) and (5–5.8′), we have

$$\frac{dH}{dt} = -\sum_{j=0}^{n} g^j \sum_{i=0}^{n} \lambda^i g_{x_j}^i + \sum_{i=0}^{n} \lambda^i \sum_{j=0}^{n} g_{x^j}^i g^j$$

$$+ \sum_{i=0}^{n} \lambda^i \sum_{j=0}^{m} g_{u^j}^i \dot u^j + \sum_{i=0}^{n} \lambda_i g_t^i.$$

But the first two terms on the right-hand side of the equation cancel; the third term is zero, because $g^i_{u^j}$ is zero unless u^j is at the boundary $u^j = 0$, so that $\dot{u}^j = 0$. In particular, $g^i_{u^j} = 0$ at any points of discontinuity of u^j, so the third term is also zero. Therefore, we are left with

$$\frac{dH}{dt} = \sum_{i=0}^{n} \lambda^i g^i_t. \qquad (5\text{-}5.14)$$

Returning now to the problem of minimizing the time required to reach a given terminal point, it is not immediately clear that it is of the type which we have been discussing, for in our discussion, T has always been a constant. Formally, we could write $\dot{x}^0 = -1$, with $x^0_0 = 0$, and then write the equations for maximizing x^0_T:

$$\frac{d\lambda^i}{dt} = -\sum_{j=1}^{n} \lambda^j g^j_{x^i} \quad \text{and} \quad \dot{x}^i = g^i, \quad i = 1, \ldots, n,$$

$$\qquad (5\text{-}5.15)$$

$$H = \sum_{j=1}^{n} \lambda^j g^j(x, u, t) = \text{maximum over } u.$$

Note that we may begin the summation with $j = 1$, not 0, because g^0 and λ^0 are both constants. Of course, this derivation is only formal: it appears to state the conditions for T to be a minimum, but T has been a given constant in all the preceding derivations. It is therefore a remarkable fact that:

A necessary condition for a policy $u(t)$, $0 \leq t \leq T$, to make $x = b$ in minimal time is that there exist functions of time, $\lambda_1(t), \ldots, \lambda_n(t)$, satisfying Eqs. (5-5.15).

Without any pretension of rigor, we shall try to make this result plausible. Let us assume that along the optimal path, $x^1(t)$ increases continuously. Then we can interchange the roles t and x^1. The problem then becomes:

minimize $\quad t_{b_1}$ (i.e., the value of t when $x^1 = b_1$)

subject to $\quad \dfrac{dt}{dx^1} = \dfrac{1}{g^1(x, u, t)},$ $\qquad (5\text{-}5.16)$

$$\frac{dx^i}{dx^1} = \frac{g^i(x, u, t)}{g^1(x, u, t)} \quad \text{for} \quad i = 2, \ldots, n, \qquad (5\text{-}5.17)$$

$u \geq 0.$

Note that now all the x^i, as well as t, are to be thought of as functions of x^1. The terminal conditions are that $x^i(b_1) = b_i$ for $i = 2, \ldots, n$. Our theory is now applicable, and we obtain the result that for optimality there must exist multipliers $\mu^1(x^1), \ldots, \mu^n(x^1)$ such that

$$\frac{d\mu^1}{dx^1} = -\mu^1 \frac{\partial}{\partial t}\left(\frac{1}{g^1}\right) - \sum_{j=2}^{n} \mu^j \frac{\partial}{\partial t} \frac{g^j}{g^1},$$

$$\frac{d\mu^i}{dx^1} = -\mu^1 \frac{\partial}{\partial x^i} \frac{1}{g^1} - \sum_{j=2}^{n} \mu^j \frac{\partial}{\partial x^i} \frac{g^j}{g^1}$$

$$= +\mu^1 \frac{g_{x^i}^1}{(g^1)^2} - \sum_{j=2}^{n} \mu^j \left[\frac{g_{x^i}^j}{g^1} - \frac{g^j}{(g^1)^2} g_{x^i}^1\right], \qquad i = 2, \ldots, n, \quad (5\text{–}5.18)$$

and

$$\frac{\partial H}{\partial u^i} = \frac{\partial}{\partial u^i}\left[\frac{\mu^1}{g^1} + \sum_{j=2}^{n} \frac{\mu^j g^j}{g^1}\right] = \frac{\mu^1}{(g^1)^2} g_{u^i}^1 - \sum_{j=2}^{n} \mu^j \left[\frac{g_{u^i}^j}{g^1} - \frac{g^j g_{u^i}^1}{(g^1)^2}\right] = 0$$

$$(5\text{–}5.19)$$

or

$$u_i = 0.$$

If we introduce new variables defined by

$$\lambda^1 \equiv -\frac{\mu^1}{g^1} - \sum_{j=2}^{n} \frac{\mu^j g^j}{g^1}, \qquad \lambda^i \equiv \mu^i, \qquad i = 2, \ldots, n,$$

Eqs. (5–5.18) become

$$g_1 \frac{d\lambda^i}{dx^1} = -\sum_{j=1}^{n} \lambda^j g_{x^i}^j, \qquad i = 2, \ldots, n.$$

But since $g^1 = dx^1/dt$, these equations give

$$\frac{d\lambda^i}{dt} = -\sum_{j=1}^{n} \lambda^j g_{x^i}^j. \qquad (5\text{–}5.20)$$

Similarly, Eqs. (5–5.19) become

$$\sum_{j=1}^{n} \lambda^j g_{u^i}^j = 0 \qquad \text{or} \qquad u_i = 0, \qquad i = 1, \ldots, m. \qquad (5\text{–}5.21)$$

We now have all of Eq. (5–5.15) except for

$$\frac{d\lambda^1}{dt} = -\sum_{j=1}^{n} \lambda^j g_{x^1}^j. \qquad (5\text{–}5.22)$$

But, on noting that $\lambda^1 = -H$ in this problem, we know that Eq. (5–5.14) applies and yields

$$\frac{d\lambda_1}{dx_1} = -\frac{dH}{dx_1} = \mu^1 \frac{\partial}{\partial x^1} \frac{1}{g^1} + \sum_{i=2}^{n} \mu^i \frac{\partial}{\partial x^1} \frac{g^i}{g^1}$$

$$= \frac{-\mu^2}{(g^1)^2} g_{x^1}^1 + \sum_{i=2}^{n} \mu^i \left[\frac{g_{x^1}^i}{g^1} - \frac{g^i}{(g^1)^2} g_{x^1}^1 \right]$$

$$= \frac{1}{g^1} \sum_{i=1}^{n} \lambda^i g_{x^1}^i,$$

from which Eq. (5–5.22) follows when we multiply both sides by g^1. The formal result stated in Eq. (5–5.12) is therefore justified. If there is no single variable which increases (or decreases) constantly along the optimal path, we can switch from one variable to another along the optimal route, for Eqs. (5–5.15) are in no way dependent upon our choice of the variable to use in the role of x^1.

Examples of the application of the maximum principle seem to fall into two groups, those which are so easy that the answer is obvious at the outset, and those which are interesting but require so much computing that they are not suitable for a textbook. We shall have to content ourselves with one from the first group and a reference to an interesting collection of problems from the second group (see the book by Fang in the Suggested Readings).

Example. Let us return to the production control problem stated previously, but let us now assume that s is a constant, $\bar{s}$, and instead of minimizing the given cost function, let us minimize the time required to reach the equilibrium position, $p = \bar{s}$ and $v = a + b\bar{s}$. Defining $x^1 = v - (a + b\bar{s})$ and $x^2 = p - \bar{s}$, we get the equations

$$\dot{x}^1 = x^2, \qquad \dot{x}^2 = u - 1, \qquad 0 \le u \le 2,$$

and we seek the policy which will bring us to the point $(0, 0)$ in minimal time. The reader should stop at this point and figure out how we can easily solve this very simple problem by common sense and a little elementary calculus. It is noteworthy, however, that the following analysis finds the same solution quite automatically. Proceeding with the analysis, we find that Eq. (5–5.14) becomes

$$\frac{d\lambda^1}{dt} = 0, \qquad \frac{d\lambda^2}{dt} = -\lambda^1,$$

and

$$\lambda^1 x^2 + \lambda^2(u - 1) \qquad \text{is maximum over} \quad 0 \le u \le 2.$$

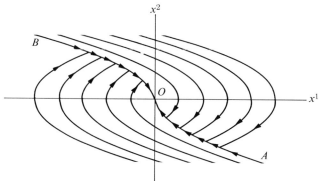

Figure 5-4

From the first of these conditions, $\lambda^1 = c_1$, a constant; and from the second, $\lambda^2 = c_2 - c_1 t$, where c_2 is another constant. From the third condition,

$$
u = \begin{cases} 2 & \text{if } \lambda^2 > 0, \\ \text{any value} & \text{if } \lambda^2 = 0, \\ 0 & \text{if } \lambda^2 < 0. \end{cases}
$$

Because λ^2 is a linear function of time, u *will change value at most once.* When $u = 2$, the x vector moves according to the equations

$$
x^2 = t + k^2,
$$

$$
x^1 = \frac{t^2}{2} + k_2 t + k_1 = \tfrac{1}{2}(t + k_2)^2 + \left(k_1 - \frac{k_2^2}{2}\right) = \tfrac{1}{2}(x^2)^2 + k_3,
$$

where k_1, k_2, and k_3 are constants. The second equation shows that in the $x^1 x^2$-plane, the "state" point moves along parabolas which have the x^1-axis as their principal axis and open to the right along it. The motion is in the direction of increasing x^2. When $u = 0$, we similarly find that motion is in the direction of decreasing x^2 along the parabolas

$$
x^2 = -\tfrac{1}{2}(x^2)^2 + k_4,
$$

which open to the left along the x^1-axis. Since we know that u changes its value only once, an optimal path changes from one set of parabolas to the other set only once. Therefore, all the optimal paths follow the pattern of the lines and arrows shown in Fig. 5–4. Thus, we have found the structure of all optimal paths, and it is never necessary to calculate the values of the λ. Note that all optimal paths come into the origin along the "arteries" AO or BO. What is the economic interpretation of this artery?

PROBLEMS

1. Write out the differential equations for the solution of the production and inventory control problem as originally stated, but assume that s is constant. What constant vector, (x, λ), is a solution of these equations? Assuming that u never is at its boundary, show that $(x, \lambda)' = ke^{rt}$, where k is a vector of constants, is a solution if r is any one of the four values of

$$c^{1/4} \left(\frac{\pm 1 \pm i}{\sqrt{2}} \right) .$$

[Note that $i = \sqrt{-1}$; recall that $(1 + i)/\sqrt{2}$ and $(-1 - i)/\sqrt{2}$ are both square roots of i.] Interpret the differential equations for the Lagrangian multipliers in this problem. (For a generalization of this problem, see the book by Kipiniak in the Suggested Readings. For an actual application, see the Holt article or the Theil book.)

2. Derive the maximum principle for the case in which there is an upper bound on the value of u.

3. How would the equations of the maximum principle be affected by an additional constraint of the form $ax_t + bu_t \leq c$, where a and b are row vectors?

CHAPTER 6

CHARACTERISTIC VALUES
OF SYMMETRIC MATRICES AND
THE THEORY OF NORMAL REGRESSION

6-1 THE PRINCIPAL AXES THEOREM

Perhaps the simplest and most frequently used nonlinear function of a single variable x is x^2, or ax^2, where a is constant. If we write $ax^2 = xax$, we immediately see that the n-dimensional generalization of this function is $x'Ax$, where x is a vector and A is a square symmetric* matrix. An expression of the form $x'Ax$ is therefore naturally called a *quadratic* form; these forms play a role in the mathematics of several variables easily as prominent as that of x^2 in the mathematics of one variable.

We can get a feeling for what a function of the sort $q = x'Ax$ "looks like" from a graph such as that shown in Fig. 6–1. We plot each point on the outer ellipse of this figure by choosing a point, x, on the unit circle in the center of the figure (where $x'x = 1$) and then marking out a length of $x'Ax$ on the ray which starts from the origin and passes through x. The point marked is therefore $(x'Ax)x$. The locus of all such points is the ellipse.

Figure 6–1 shows the ellipse generated in this way by the quadratic form

$$z = x' \begin{pmatrix} \frac{66}{25} & \frac{12}{25} \\ \frac{12}{25} & \frac{59}{25} \end{pmatrix} x,$$

where the x-vector is the representation of a point relative to the axis vectors

---

* No functions of x can be expressed by $x'Ax$ with A nonsymmetric which cannot also be expressed with a symmetric matrix, for if $x'Ax$ contains the sum

$$a_{ij}x_ix_j + a_{ji}x_jx_i = (a_{ji} + a_{ji})x_ix_j,$$

with $a_{ij} \neq a_{ji}$, then we can define

$$b_{ij} = b_{ji} = (a_{ij} + a_{ji})/2.$$

Then the B-matrix is symmetric, and $x'Bx = x'Ax$ for all values of x.

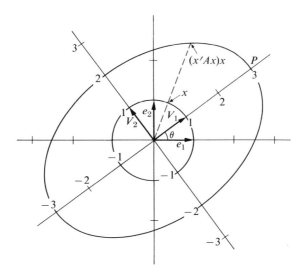

Figure 6–1

e_1 and e_2. If we let y be the representation of points relative to the axis vectors V_1 and V_2 of Fig. 6–1, then we see from the form of the graph that this *same* ellipse is given by the quadratic form

$$z = y' \begin{pmatrix} 3 & 0 \\ 0 & 2 \end{pmatrix} y = 3y_1^2 + 2y_2^2.$$

Thus, relative to the proper *orthogonal* axis system, the quadratic function can be expressed as a weighted sum of squares. The V_1- and V_2-vectors are therefore quite naturally known as the *principal axes* of the ellipse.

Clearly, such a simplification can be useful in theoretical investigations, and subsequent sections will show it to be very valuable indeed. The job of the present section is to formulate and prove the basic theorem about the possibility of this simplification.

In order to formulate the theorem, we must first discover how to express algebraically the condition that two vectors are orthogonal, that is, perpendicular to each other. In two dimensions, the law of cosines* states that if O, a, and b are the vertices of a triangle (see Fig. 6–2) and if the length of a

---

* The law of cosines can be derived from the Pythagorean Theorem and the definitions of the sine and cosine functions. In Fig. 6–3, $h = b \sin \theta$, $x = b \cos \theta$, and

$$\begin{aligned} c^2 &= h^2 + (a - x)^2 = h^2 + x^2 + a^2 - 2ax \\ &= b^2 \sin^2 \theta + b^2 \cos^2 \theta + a^2 - 2ab \cos \theta \\ &= a^2 + b^2 - 2ab \cos \theta, \end{aligned}$$

since $\sin^2 \theta + \cos^2 \theta = 1$ for all θ.

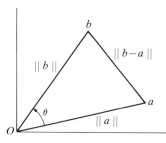

Figure 6-2

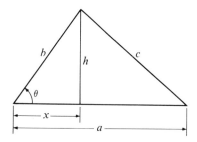

Figure 6-3

vector, say a, is denoted by $\|a\| = \sqrt{a'a}$, then

$$\|b - a\|^2 = \|a\|^2 + \|b\|^2 - 2\|a\| \cdot \|b\| \cos \theta, \qquad (6\text{-}1.1)$$

where θ is the angle between a and b, But

$$\|b - a\|^2 = (b - a)'(b - a) = a'a - 2a'b + b'b = \|a\|^2 + \|b\|^2 - 2a'b.$$
$$(6\text{-}1.2)$$

Comparison of the right-hand sides of (6–1.1) and (6–1.2) shows that

$$-2a'b = 2\|a\| \cdot \|b\| \cos \theta$$

or

$$\cos \theta = \frac{a'b}{\|a\| \cdot \|b\|}. \qquad (6\text{-}1.3)$$

When $\theta = \pm 90°$, $\cos \theta = 0$, so $a'b = 0$. Therefore, we adopt the following definition:

Two vectors, a and b, are said to be *orthogonal* if $a'b = 0$. A matrix V such that $V'V = I$ is said to be orthogonal; this condition implies that all its columns are mutually orthogonal.

We can now formulate and prove the n-dimensional version of the simplification theorem.

Theorem 6-1 (*The Principal Axes Theorem*). If A is a symmetric matrix, then there exists a matrix V such that $V'V = I$ and

$$V'AV = D, \qquad (6\text{-}1.4)$$

where D is a diagonal matrix.

Note that by the change of variables $x = Vy$, the quadratic form $x'Ax$ becomes $y'V'AVy = y'Dy$. That is, the columns of V are the principal axes of the quadratic form using the A-matrix.

Proof. Subject to the constraint $x'x = 1$, the function $Q = x'Ax$ has a maximum at some point, and we know that at that point the derivative of the Lagrangian expression

$$L = x'Ax - \lambda(x'x - 1)$$

must be equal to zero:

$$2Ax - 2\lambda x = 0.$$

That is, we know that there exists a vector x and a scalar λ satisfying the equation

$$Ax = \lambda x. \tag{6–1.5}$$

A λ and an x satisfying (6–1.5) are called a *characteristic value* of A and an associated *characteristic vector*, respectively. The λ is the value of the quadratic form at x: $Q = x'Ax = x'\lambda x = \lambda$. Let us call this maximum value λ_1 and its associated characteristic vector V_1, where $V_1'V_1 = 1$. In Fig. 6–1, V_1 is marked, and λ_1 is the length of the longest radius of the ellipse.

If the dimension of A is greater than 2, we can proceed to maximize Q subject to two constraints:

$$x'x = 1 \quad \text{and} \quad x'V_1 = 0.$$

(That is, x is orthogonal to V_1.) As before, a maximum must exist and must make the derivative of the Lagrangian

$$L = x'Ax - \lambda(x'x - 1) - \mu_1(x'V_1)$$

equal to zero:

$$2Ax - 2\lambda x - \mu_1 V_1 = 0. \tag{6–1.6}$$

We shall see that in fact $\mu_1 = 0$, for on premultiplying (6–1.6) by V_1', we find that

$$2V_1'Ax - 2\lambda V_1'x - \mu_1 V_1'V_1 = 0. \tag{6–1.7}$$

Since $A = A'$, it follows that

$$V_1'A = (AV_1)' = \lambda_1 V_1',$$

so (6–1.7) becomes

$$2\lambda_1 V_1'x - 2\lambda V_1'x - \mu_1 V_1'V_1 = 0.$$

But because $V_1'x = 0$ and $V_1'V_1 = 1$, this equation reduces to $\mu_1 = 0$. Therefore (6–1.6) becomes simply

$$Ax = \lambda x, \tag{6–1.8}$$

which is the same as (6–1.5), but we now know that there is a solution of (6–1.8), say λ_2 and V_2, such that $V_2'V_1 = 0$ and $\lambda_2 = V_2'AV_2 \le \lambda_1$.

If the dimension of A is greater than 3, we continue on to maximize Q subject to $x'V_1 = 0$, $x'V_2 = 0$, and $x'x = 1$. In place of (6–1.6) we would find

$$2Ax - 2\lambda x - \mu_1 V_1 - \mu_2 V_2 = 0. \tag{6–1.9}$$

Multiplying first by V_1' and then by V_2', we see that μ_1 and $\mu_2 = 0$, so that there exists a λ_3 and V_3 with $\lambda_3 \le \lambda_2$ and $V_3'V_1 = 0$, $V_3'V_2 = 0$, and $V_3'V_3 = 1$.

If A is of dimension n, then we can continue this process until we have found $V_1, V_2, \ldots, V_{n-1}$. But when we look for a vector orthogonal to all these $n - 1$ vectors, we find that we have $n - 1$ equations for the n elements of such a vector. Therefore, all such vectors are scalar multiples of a single vector, V_n. Is V_n a characteristic vector of A? Yes, for if $i < n$, then

$$V_i'(AV_n) = (V_i'A)V_n = (A'V_i)'V_n = (AV_i)'V_n = \lambda_i V_i'V_n = 0.$$

Thus AV_n is orthogonal to all the $V_1, \ldots, V_{n-1}$. But we have just observed that all such vectors are multiples of a single vector V_n. Therefore $AV_n = \lambda_n V_n$.

Hence we have found a matrix $V = (V_1, \ldots, V_n)$ such that $V'V = I$ and

$$AV = (\lambda_1 V_1, \lambda_2 V_2, \ldots, \lambda_n V_n). \tag{6–1.10}$$

Multiplying (6–1.10) on the left by V' gives

$$V'AV = \begin{pmatrix} \lambda_1 & 0 \ldots 0 \\ 0 & \lambda_2 \ldots 0 \\ \vdots & \vdots \\ 0 & 0 \ldots \lambda_n \end{pmatrix} = D,$$

and thus completes the proof.

In connection with the second-order maximum conditions, we defined a *positive definite matrix* as a symmetric matrix A such that

$$x'Ax > 0 \quad \text{if} \quad x \ne 0.$$

A positive semidefinite matrix is a matrix A such that $x'Ax \ge 0$ for all x. As an immediate corollary of the principal axes theorem, we have

Theorem 6–2. A symmetric matrix A is positive definite if and only if all its characteristic values are positive. It is positive semidefinite if and only if all its characteristic values are nonnegative.

The proof is left as an exercise. The following theorem will prove useful in Section 6–3.

Theorem 6–3. A symmetric matrix A is positive semidefinite if and only if there exists a matrix B such that $A = B'B$.

Proof. If $A = B'B$, then

$$x'Ax = x'B'Bx = (Bx)'(Bx) \geq 0,$$

since $(Bx)'(Bx)$ is just a sum of squares. On the other hand, if A is positive semidefinite, then by the principal axes theorem, $A = V'DV$, where D is diagonal with nonnegative elements. Therefore $D = R'R$, where R is a diagonal matrix with $r_{ii} = \sqrt{d_{ii}}$. Therefore

$$A = V'R'RV = (RV)'(RV),$$

and letting $B = RV$ completes the proof.

The following two theorems concern inverse matrices.

Theorem 6–4. If λ is a characteristic value of A, λ^{-1} is a characteristic value of A^{-1}. (A need not be symmetric in this theorem.)

Theorem 6–5. If A is positive definite, so is A^{-1}.

The proofs of both these theorems are short and are left as exercises.

PROBLEMS

1. Show that the sum of the characteristic values of a symmetric matrix equals its trace.

2. Show that if $A = A'$ and $AA = A$, then all the characteristic roots of A are 0 or 1.

3. Prove (a) Theorem 6–2, (b) Theorem 6–4, (c) Theorem 6–5.

4. Show that 0 is a characteristic root of a matrix if and only if the matrix is singular.

5. Show that if A is a positive definite matrix, then there exists a matrix P such that $P'AP = I$.

6. Show that a positive definite matrix is nonsingular.

7. Show that if A and B are square matrices of the same size and λ is a characteristic value of AB, then λ is also a characteristic value of BA [A and B do not have to be symmetric; use Eq. (6–1.5)].

6–2 COMPUTING CHARACTERISTIC VALUES AND VECTORS.
ORTHOGONAL REGRESSIONS

The principal axes theorem is often used in the derivation of formulas which do not require the calculation of the characteristic values or vectors. Some applications, however, do require this computation. Suppose, for example, that we wanted to sum up two observations on a person, his height and his weight, by a single measure. In Fig. 6–4, the point x_1 represents the two attributes for man number 1, and t_1, the distance from the origin to the base of the perpendicular going off to x_1, is the single measure of how "big" this man is. We seek the line which minimizes the sum of the squares of the *distances* of the eight plotted points from the line, with distances measured perpendicularly to the line, not vertically, as in ordinary regression. This sort of problem is known as orthogonal regression. Whereas ordinary regression is used to predict one variable from others, orthogonal regression is useful for describing and summarizing data. In this role, it is often referred to as factor analysis.

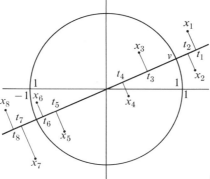

Figure 6–4

   The units and origin for measuring each attribute are chosen so that the mean of each attribute is zero and its variance is one. The orthogonal regressional line is determined by the origin and the point v on the unit circle, that is, $v'v = 1$. The point $t_i v$ is the "foot" of the perpendicular from x_i. Given a v, what is the sum of squares of the perpendicular distances from the points to the line v determines? To answer this question, we note that t_i is chosen so as to minimize* the square of the distance from x_i to tv, namely

$$(x_i - t_i v)'(x_i - t_i v) = x_i'x_i - 2t_i x_i'v + v'v t_i^2.$$

* The *shortest* distance from a point to a line is along a *perpendicular* to the line.

We set the derivative of this expression with respect to t_i equal to zero and find

$$t_i = x_i'v/v'v = x_i'v,$$

since $v'v = 1$.

If we now let t denote the vector of t_i's, $t = Xv$, where X' is the matrix with x_i as its ith column, we see that the sum of the squares of the perpendiculars is the sum of the squares of the elements of the matrix $X - tv' = X - (Xv)v'$. But the sum of the squares of the elements of any matrix, A, is given by tr $A'A$. Therefore, the sum of squares of perpendiculars is

$$
\begin{aligned}
\text{tr}\,[(X - (Xv)v')(X' - v(v'X'))] \\
= \text{tr}\,(XX' - Xvv'X' - Xvv'X' + Xvv'vv'X') \\
= \text{tr}\,(XX' - Xvv'X) \quad &(\text{since } v'v = 1) \\
= \text{tr}\,XX' - \text{tr}\,Xvv'X' \quad &(\text{tr}\,(A + B) = \text{tr}\,A + \text{tr}\,B) \\
= \text{tr}\,XX' - \text{tr}\,v'X'Xv \quad &(\text{since tr}\,AB = \text{tr}\,BA) \\
= \text{tr}\,XX' - v'X'Xv \quad &(\text{since } v'X'Xv \text{ is a scalar}).
\end{aligned}
$$

The v we seek minimizes this sum of the squares of perpendiculars and therefore maximizes $v'X'Xv$ subject to $v'v = 1$. Hence v is the characteristic vector corresponding to the largest characteristic value of the symmetric matrix $X'X$.* Thus we are led to wish for a way of actually calculating characteristic values and vectors.

For a symmetric matrix A for which $\lambda_1 > \lambda_2$, a simple iterative method of approximating V_1 and λ_1 can be used. To begin the method, choose an arbitrary initial vector, u^0, and define $u^{(m)}$ recursively by $u^{(m)} = Au^{(m-1)}$. We shall show that

$$V_1 = \lim_{m \to \infty} \frac{u^{(m)}}{\|u^{(m)}\|}, \qquad \text{where} \qquad \|u\| = \sqrt{u'u}. \tag{6–2.1}$$

That is, as we take higher and higher values of m, $u^{(m)}/\|u^{(m)}\|$ becomes an increasingly good approximation of V_1.

Let us define a vector c by $u^0 = Vc$, where the $V = (V_1, \ldots, V_n)$ is the (unknown) matrix of characteristic vectors of A. Then

$$Au^0 = AVc = \sum_{j=1}^{n} c_j AV_j = \sum_{j=1}^{n} c_j \lambda_j V_j.$$

Then by the definition of $u^{(m)}$,

$$u^{(m)} = \sum_{j=1}^{n} c_j \lambda_j^m V_j. \tag{6–2.2}$$

---

* In factor analysis or principal component analysis, this v is called the first factor loading or first component; the v with the next largest characteristic root is the second factor or component, and so on.

Now because $\lambda_1 > \lambda_2 \geq \lambda_3 \geq \cdots \geq \lambda_n$, dividing (6-2.2) by $c_1\lambda_1^m$ shows that

$$\lim_{m\to\infty} \left(\frac{u^{(m)}}{c_1\lambda_1^m}\right) = V_1. \tag{6-2.3}$$

We now define $k_m = \|u^{(m)}\|/c_1\lambda_1^{(m)}$. Then $\lim_{m\to\infty} |k_m| = 1$, for by (6-2.3),

$$\lim_{m\to\infty} |k_m| = \lim_{m\to\infty} \left\| \frac{u^{(m)}}{c_1\lambda_1^m} \right\| = \|V_1\| = 1.$$

Hence

$$V_1 = \lim_{m\to\infty} k_m \frac{u^{(m)}}{\|u^{(m)}\|} = \pm 1 \lim_{m\to\infty} \frac{u^{(m)}}{\|u^{(m)}\|},$$

which establishes (6-2.1). (Either the plus or the minus may be taken.) Since

$$\lim_{m\to\infty} \frac{u^{(m+1)}}{\|u^{(m)}\|} = \lim_{m\to\infty} \frac{Au^{(m)}}{\|u^{(m)}\|} = AV_1 = \lambda_1 V_1 = \lambda_1 \lim_{m\to\infty} \frac{u^{(m)}}{\|u^{(m)}\|},$$

we also have

$$\lim_{m\to\infty} \frac{u_i^{(m+1)}}{u_i^{(m)}} = \lambda_1 \quad \text{for} \quad i = 1, \ldots, n.$$

We can use the degree of agreement among these ratios to decide how long to continue increasing m.

Example. Find λ_1 for

$$A = \begin{pmatrix} 2 & 1 \\ 1 & 3 \end{pmatrix}.$$

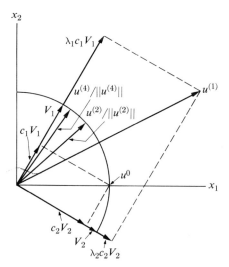

Choose $u^0 = e_1$. The subsequent $u^{(m)}$ and the ratios $u_1^{(m+1)}/u_i^{(m)}$ are given in Table 6-1. We find $V_1' \approx (0.52, 0.85)$ and $\lambda_1 \approx 3.618$. Figure 6-5 shows u^0 and $u^{(1)}$ and their representations as

$$u^0 = c_1V_1 + c_2V_2$$

and

$$u^{(1)} = \lambda_1c_1V_1 + \lambda_2c_2V_2.$$

These representations show clearly how the larger λ, λ_1, "pulls" $u^{(m)}$ toward the direction of V_1.

Figure 6-5

Table 6–1

m	0	1	2	3	4	5	6	7	8	9
$u^{(m)}$	1	2	5	15	50	175	625	2,250	8,125	29,375
	0	1	5	20	75	275	1,000	3,625	13,125	47,500
Ratios		2	2.5	3	3.33	3.5	3.57	3.60	3.611	3.615
		∞	5	4	3.75	3.67	3.64	3.625	3.621	3.619

PROBLEMS

1. Perform an orthogonal regression on the X_3 and y of Table 2–1.

2. One method of finding λ_2 and V_2 of a symmetric matrix A is to use the equation $V_1'x = 0$ to eliminate x_1 in the quadratic form $x'Ax$. What will be the new quadratic form in $x_2, \ldots, x_n$? Why will its largest characteristic value be λ_2? How can V_2 be calculated? Extend this method to λ_3, λ_4, etc.

6–3 NORMAL REGRESSION

Some of the most important applications of the principal axes theorem arise in the theory of testing hypotheses by regression analysis. In these applications, it is not necessary to actually calculate the characteristic roots and vectors; the knowledge that they exist justifies the application of the tests we wish to use.

Economic hypotheses can often be framed in terms of a regression coefficient being zero. For an illustration, we may return to the example of Sections 2–1 and 2–2. In terms of the β-vector (the true coefficients), the hypothesis that phosphates have no effect on yield becomes the assumption that $\beta_2 = 0$, while the hypothesis that nitrates have no effect on yield becomes $\beta_3 = 0$. The test of the phosphate hypothesis consists of answering the question, "If the hypothesis is true, what is the probability that we should find a value of b_2 as high as that which we actually found in our sample?" If the answer is "Quite high, namely 0.6," we would conclude that we could not reject the hypothesis of "no effect from phosphates." But if the answer is "Very low, namely 0.02," we would feel justified in rejecting the hypothesis. Of course, we may be wrong in rejecting the hypothesis, so it is customary to hedge our rejection by saying that we reject the hypothesis "with 98 percent confidence" or that the regression coefficient is "significantly different from zero at the 2 percent level of significance."

In this approach to hypothesis testing, a hypothesis is either true or not true; no probability is attached to its truth. We reject the hypothesis, however, when it implies that a very improbable event has happened before our very eyes. Much empirical work in economics, therefore, takes the rather peculiar form of a search for hypotheses which can be rejected! For if a hypothesis of "no effect" can be rejected, the opposite or hypothesis of "some effect" must be accepted. Hence, by rejecting the hypothesis of no effect, we demonstrate that certain variables affect others.

The Multivariate Normal Distribution

From the mathematical point of view, the testing of hypotheses becomes the calculation of the probability distributions of the regression coefficients, b, or of other statistics, under the assumption that one or more elements of the β-vector are zero. To make such calculations, we must obviously make some assumptions about the only random part of the regression equation

$$y = X\beta + e, \tag{6–3.1}$$

namely, about the vector of errors, e. In Chapter 2, we assumed that the X-matrix is predetermined and not random and that all the elements of e are independent, have zero means, and have the same variance, σ^2. In other words, $E(e) = 0$ and $E(ee') = \sigma^2 I_T$. To these assumptions we now add only the assumption that each of the elements is normally distributed, that is, that its probability density function is

$$f(x) = ce^{-x^2/2\sigma^2}, \tag{6–3.2}$$

where c is a constant determined so that $\int_{-\infty}^{\infty} f(x)\,dx = 1$. Such a variable has mean 0 and variance σ^2; for short, it is said to be normal $(0, \sigma^2)$. With this additional assumption, Eq. (6–3.1) is said to be a normal regression equation.

Since b, the least-squares estimate of β, is

$$b = (X'X)^{-1}X'y = (X'X)^{-1}X'(XB + e) = \beta + (X'X)^{-1}X'e,$$

the difference between an element of b and the corresponding element of β is a *linear transformation of the normal variables e.* What is the distribution of linear transformations of independent normal variables? To answer this basic question, we shall need to use two fundamental techniques.

a) *Change of variable technique.* If $f(x)$ is the density function of x, then the density function of a new variable y related to x by $x = h(y)$, with $h'(y) > 0$ for all y, is given by $g(y) = f(h(y))h'(y)$.

Proof. If $x_i = h(y_i)$, $i = 1, 2$, then

$$P(y_1 \le y \le y_2) = P(x_1 \le x \le x_2) = \int_{x_1}^{x_2} f(x)\,dx$$

$$= \int_{y_1}^{y_2} f(h(y))h'(y)\,dy,$$

where the second equality follows from the definition of the density function (see Section 1–8) and the last equality follows from the standard calculus formula for substitution in definite integrals. When the transformation is linear, $x = h(y) = cy + b$, then $h'(x)$ is just a constant, so $g(y) = cf(h(y))$. When x and y are vectors, $x = Cy$, we can make the transformation by taking one variable at a time: we first substitute for x_1 in terms of y_1 and $x_2, \ldots, x_n$, then for x_2 in terms of y_2, y_1, and $x_3, \ldots, x_n$, etc. Here again $g(y) = cf(h(y))$, where c is some constant. (To be precise, it is the determinant of the matrix C; see the appendix on determinants.)

b) *Elimination by integration technique.* If $f(x, y)$ is the joint density function of x and y, the density function of x alone is $g(x) = \int_{-\infty}^{\infty} f(x, y) \, dy$, for

$$P\left(\begin{matrix} x_1 \leq x \leq x_2 \\ \text{while} \\ -\infty < y < \infty \end{matrix}\right) = \int_{x_1}^{x_2} \int_{-\infty}^{\infty} f(x, y) \, dx \, dy = \int_{x_1}^{x_2} g(x) \, dx,$$

where the first equality follows from the definition of the joint density function (see Section 2–2) and the second equality follows from the standard iterated integral method of evaluating multiple integrals.

We now apply these techniques to the calculation of the joint frequency density function of a *vector* y of n variables which are linear combinations of the m independent variables x which are all normal (0, 1). We assume that $n \leq m$. By the definition of "independent" variables (see Section 2–2), the joint density function of the x-variables is the product of the individual density functions:

$$f(x_1, \ldots, x_m) = ce^{-x_1^2/2}e^{-x_2^2/2} \cdots e^{-x_m^2/2} = ce^{-x'x/2}. \qquad (6\text{–}3.3)$$

The vector y is defined in terms of x by the equation

$$y = Cx, \qquad (6\text{–}3.4)$$

where the matrix C is n by m. We shall suppose that the first n columns of C constitute a nonsingular matrix. Let us divide the x-vector into two parts, and let us call the first n elements u and the remaining elements v, that is,

$$x = \begin{pmatrix} u \\ v \end{pmatrix}.$$

Equation (6–3.4) can then be solved for u to give

$$u = Ay + Bv, \qquad (6\text{–}3.5)$$

where A is a nonsingular, n-by-n matrix (the inverse of the first m columns of

C) and B is n by $(m - n)$. If $m = n$, the Bv-term in (6–3.5) disappears, as do all the terms involving v in the following formulas, which would thereby only be simplified.

Since

$$x'x = u'u + v'v = (y'A' + v'B')(Ay + Bv) + v'v,$$

the change of variable rule applied to (6–3.3) shows that the joint frequency function of y and v is

$$f(y, v) = c' \exp\left[-\left((y'A' + v'B')(Ay + Bv) + v'v\right)/2\right]$$
$$= c' \exp\left[-(y'A'Ay + y'A'Bv + v'B'Ay + v'B'Bv + v'v)/2\right],$$

$$(6\text{–}3.6)$$

where $\exp k$ means e^k. If $m = n$, Eq. (6–3.6) becomes

$$f(y) = c' \exp\left[-y'A'Ay/2\right], \tag{6–3.6'}$$

and our mission is accomplished. We continue with the $n < m$ case.

We now wish to integrate out all variables other than the y's. We can easily accomplish this task if we can separate the y's from the other variables, and the principal axes theorem is just what we need for the job. This is because if $v \neq 0$, $v'(I + B'B)v = v'v + (Bv)'(Bv) > 0$, the symmetric matrix $I + B'B$ is positive definite and Theorem 6–3 assures the existence of a matrix P such that

$$PP' = I + B'B. \tag{6–3.7}$$

We can then replace v in (6–3.6) by a new variable, w, defined by

$$w = (P^{-1})B'Ay + P'v.$$

With this transformation, (6–3.6) becomes

$$f(y, w) = c'' \exp\left[-(y'A'Ay - y'A'B(P^{-1})'P^{-1}B'Ay + w'w)/2\right].$$

(Essentially, we have just applied a matrix generalization of the technique of "completing the square," familiar from quadratic equations of high school algebra.)

We can now integrate out the w-variables and obtain the joint density function of the y's,

$$f(y) = c''' \exp\left[-y'(A'A - A'B(P^{-1})'P^{-1}B'A)y/2\right]$$
$$= c'''e^{-y'Qy/2}, \tag{6–3.8}$$

where the last equation serves to define the matrix Q. We shall show that Q

is positive definite. First, since $(P^{-1})' = (P')^{-1}$, Eq. (6–3.7) implies that $(P^{-1})'P^{-1} = (P')^{-1}P^{-1} = (I + B'B)^{-1}$, so

$$Q = A'(I - B(I + B'B)^{-1}B')A = A'(I + BB')^{-1}A. \qquad (6–3.9)$$

[The second of these equalities requires the reader to verify by direct multiplication that $(I - B(I + B'B)^{-1}B')(I + BB') = I$.]   Since $I + BB'$ is positive definite, so is its inverse. If $y \neq 0$, then $Ay \neq 0$, since A is non-singular. Therefore, if $y \neq 0$, then

$$y'Qy = y'A'(I + BB')^{-1}Ay > 0,$$

so Q is positive definite.

We have therefore proved the following theorem:

Theorem 6–6. If m variables y are related to n independent normal $(0, 1)$ variables x by $y = Cx$, $n \geq m$, and C is of rank m, then the joint density function of y is of the form

$$f(y) = ce^{-y'Qy/2}, \qquad (6–3.10)$$

where Q is positive definite.

We need a name for the joint density function given by (6–3.10), and Theorem 6–6 suggests the natural name, *the multivariate normal distribution*. We shall say that *any* variables with the density function given by (6–3.10) with a positive definite Q are normally distributed.

Theorem 6–7. Any n normally distributed variables y are linear combinations of n independent normal $(0, 1)$ variables x.

Proof. By the principal axes theorem, there exists a matrix P such that $P'QP = I$.   By the change-of-variable rule, the variables x defined by $y = Px$ or $x = P^{-1}y$ have the distribution

$$f(x) = c'e^{-x'P'QPx/2} = c'e^{-x'x/2}.$$

Therefore, the x's are independent and normal $(0, 1)$, and the y's are linear combinations of them.   Q.E.D.

Theorem 6–8. Linearly independent linear combinations of normal variables are normal.

Proof. Let y be normal and $z = Cy$. By Theorem 6–7, $y = Px$, where the x's are independent and normal $(0, 1)$.   Then $z = CPx$, and hence, by Theorem 6–6, z is normal.

Theorem 6–9. The matrix of variances and covariances of the normal variables y with the density function $f(y) = c\, e^{-y'Qy/2}$ is Q^{-1}.

Proof. The definition of the variance-covariance matrix, Σ, is

$$\Sigma = E[(y - E(y))(y - E(y))'].$$

Since, by Theorem 6–7, $y = Px$, where the x are normal $(0, 1)$ and $P'QP = I$, we find that

$$E(y) = E(Px) = PE(x) = PO = 0,$$

so

$$\Sigma = E(yy') = E(Pxx'P') = PE(xx')P' = PIP' = PP'. \qquad (6\text{–}3.11)$$

But since $P'QP = I$, we have

$$QP = (P')^{-1}, \qquad Q = (P')^{-1}P^{-1},$$

and

$$Q^{-1} = PP'. \qquad (6\text{–}3.12)$$

Combining (6–3.11) and (6–3.12) gives

$$\Sigma = Q^{-1}. \qquad \text{Q.E.D.} \qquad (6\text{–}3.13)$$

Because of this theorem, variables with the density function given in Eq. (6–3.10) are said to be normal $(0, Q^{-1})$.

Theorem 6–10. Normal variables are independent if and only if they have zero covariances.

Proof. They are independent if and only if Q is diagonal, but Q is diagonal if and only if its inverse, S, is diagonal, that is, by Theorem 6–9, if and only if the covariances, the off-diagonal elements of S, are all zero. Q.E.D.

In Chapter 2, we showed that independence always implies zero covariance, but the reverse is not generally true. However, as Theorem 6–10 shows, it is true for normal variables.

Test of Significance of a Regression Coefficient

From Theorem 6–9, we see that the deviations of the estimated regression coefficients b of a normal regression equation from their expected values, β,

$$b - \beta = (X'X)^{-1}X'e,$$

are normal $(0, \Sigma)$, where $\Sigma = \sigma^2(X'X)^{-1}$. If we knew σ^2, we could immediately test the hypothesis that any element of b, say b_i, is zero, for under the hypothesis that $\beta_i = 0$, the variable $t = b_i/\sqrt{\Sigma_{ii}}$ is normal $(0, 1)$. If this variable has a surprising value, we reject the hypothesis. (A good rule of thumb to remember is that a normal $(0, 1)$ variable is less than 2 in absolute value with probability 0.95.)

But in fact, σ^2 is almost never known and must be estimated from the residuals, r. In Chapter 2, we found that an unbiased estimate of σ^2 is given by $s^2 = r'r/(T - n)$. It is therefore natural to consider the best guess we can make of the variable t defined above, namely $t = b_i/\sqrt{S_{ii}}$, where $S = s^2(X'X)^{-1}$. What distribution will t have? To answer this question, we must first find out what distribution s^2 or $r'r$ has. Now

$$r = y - Xb = X\beta + e - X[(X'X)^{-1}X'(X\beta + e)] = [I - X(X'X)^{-1}X']e;$$
$$(6\text{-}3.14)$$

therefore the residuals, like the regression coefficients, are normally distributed.

Theorem 6–11. The residuals from a normal regression are distributed independently of the estimates of the regression coefficients.

Proof. Since both r and $b - \beta$ are normal, Theorem 6-10 tells us that to prove their independence it is sufficient to prove that their covariances are all zero. The matrix of these covariances is

$$E(r(b - \beta)') = E[(e - X(X'X)^{-1}X'e)(e'X(X'X)^{-1})]$$
$$= \sigma^2 IX(X'X)^{-1} - X(X'X)^{-1}X'\sigma^2 IX(X'X)^{-1}$$
$$= \sigma^2 X(X'X)^{-1} - \sigma^2 X(X'X)^{-1} = 0. \qquad \text{Q.E.D.}$$

Theorem 6–12. The sum of squares of the T residuals, $r'r$, from a normal regression with n independent variables has the same distribution as the sum of squares of $T - n$ independent variables which are normal $(0, \sigma^2)$.

Proof. By Eq. (2–2.9),
$$r'r = e'(I_T - B)e, \qquad (6\text{-}3.15)$$

where $B = X(X'X)^{-1}X'$, $B = B'$, and $B'B = B$. Since B is symmetric, $B^2 = B'B = B$. Our strategy is to apply the principal axes theorem to the expression on the right-hand side of (6–3.15) to convert it into a sum of squares of independent variables. The matrix $I - B$, however, has an important property which we must first note. Any matrix A satisfying the equation $A^2 = A$ is said to be *idempotent*. Thus, B is idempotent, and so is $(I_T - B)$, for

$$(I - B)(I - B) = I - B - B + BB = I - B - B + B = I - B.$$
$$(6\text{-}3.16)$$

This equation also shows that $I - B$ is positive semidefinite, and therefore the principal axes theorem provides a matrix P such that $P' = P^{-1}$ and $P'(I - B)P = D$. Now the characteristic roots λ of a symmetric idempotent matrix A are either 0 or 1, for if

$$Av = \lambda v,$$

then

$$AAv = \lambda Av, \qquad Av = \lambda Av, \qquad \lambda v = \lambda^2 v;$$

so $\lambda = \lambda^2$, which implies that $\lambda = 0$ or $\lambda = 1$. Therefore the roots of $I - B$ are either 0 or 1; that is, the elements of D are 0 or 1. The number of 1's is equal to the trace of D and

$$\begin{aligned}
\operatorname{tr} D &= \operatorname{tr} \left(P'(I_T - B)P \right) = \operatorname{tr} (I_T - P'BP) \\
&= \operatorname{tr} I_T - \operatorname{tr} PP'B = \operatorname{tr} I_T - \operatorname{tr} B.
\end{aligned}$$

But in Eq. (2-2.9), it was shown that $\operatorname{tr} B = n$, so

$$\operatorname{tr} D = T - n.$$

Therefore D has $(T - n)$ 1's and n 0's on its diagonal. For convenience, we may suppose that it is the first $(T - n)$ elements which are 1.

Now when we substitute for e in Eq. (6-3.15) the variables u defined as

$$u = P'e \qquad \text{or} \qquad Pu = e,$$

Eq. (6-3.15) becomes

$$r'r = u'P'(I - B)Pu = u'Du = \sum_{i=1}^{T-n} u_i^2.$$

But the u variables, like the e's, are independent and normal $(0, \sigma^2)$, for by the substitution rule, it follows from the density function of the e's that the density function of the u's is

$$f(u) = c'e^{-u'P'Pu/2\sigma^2} = ce^{-u'u/2\sigma^2}.$$

The proof is therefore complete.

The distribution of the sum of squares of m independent normal $(0, 1)$ variables is known as the *chi-square* (or χ^2) distribution with m degrees of freedom. (Its density function is derived in the appendix to this chapter.) We can therefore express Theorem 6–12 by saying that in a normal regression, $r'r/\sigma^2$ has a chi-square distribution with $T - n$ degrees of freedom.

The statistic we proposed for testing the hypothesis that $\beta_i = 0$ was

$$t_i = \frac{b_i}{\sqrt{S_{ii}}} = \frac{b_i}{\sqrt{a_{ii}r'r/(T - n)}} = \frac{b_i/\sigma\sqrt{a_{ii}}}{\sqrt{r'r/\sigma^2(T - n)}},$$

where a_{ii} denotes the ith diagonal element of $(X'X)^{-1}$. Since the standard error of b_i is $\sigma\sqrt{a_{ii}}$, the assumption that $\beta_i = 0$ implies that $b_i/\sigma\sqrt{a_{ii}}$, the numerator of the last expression for t_i, is a normal $(0, 1)$ variable. The denominator is the square root of a chi-square variable divided by its degree of freedom, and the numerator and denominator are independent. Such a ratio is called a *Student t*-variable with $T - n$ degrees of freedom.

More formally, if v^2 has a chi-square distribution with m degrees of freedom and u is normal $(0, 1)$ and independent of v^2, then

$$t = \frac{u}{\sqrt{v^2/m}}$$

is a Student t-variable with m degrees of freedom. Its density function is derived in the appendix to this chapter, and is tabulated in most statistics books. For values of m greater than about 30, it is practically indistinguishable from the distribution of a normal $(0, 1)$ variable.

To test the hypothesis that $\beta_i = 0$, we calculate t_i, and ask how probable it is that we should observe so large a value of t. For example, to test whether phosphates have any effect on yields in the example used in the text of Chapter 2, the null hypothesis is that $\beta_2 = 0$, and we compute

$$t_2 = 0.61/0.20 = 3.05.$$

This t-variable has two degrees of freedom $(T = 5, n = 3)$. From the tables of the Student t-distribution we find that there is only a 0.05 probability that t will exceed 2.92. Therefore, we can reject the hypothesis of no effect from phosphates with more than 95 percent confidence.

PROBLEMS

1. At what level of confidence can the hypothesis of "no effect from nitrates" be rejected?
2. Are the coefficients of the regressions calculated in Problems 1 and 2 of Section 2–1 significant at the 5 percent level?

6–4 ANALYSIS OF VARIANCE AND COVARIANCE AND THE *F*-STATISTIC

Tests of Homogeneity

Tests of the homogeneity of a population can be formulated as tests that not one but several elements of a β-vector are zero. Let us consider the following example.

Table 6-2

Group	Age of head of household	Dependent variable	Independent variables												
		y	X_1	X_2	X_3	X_4	X_5	X_6	X_7	X_8	u_1	u_2	u_3	u_4
1.	0–25	y_1	1	x_1	0	0	0	0	0	0	1	0	0	0
		$\vdots$	$\vdots$	$\vdots$					$\vdots$		$\vdots$			$\vdots$
		y_{20}	1	x_{20}	0	0	0	0	0	0	1	0	0	0
2.	26–35	y_{21}	1	x_{21}	0	1	0	0	x_{21}	0	0	1	0	0
		$\vdots$	$\vdots$	$\vdots$					$\vdots$		$\vdots$			$\vdots$
		y_{45}	1	x_{45}	0	1	0	0	x_{45}	0	0	1	0	0
3.	36–50	y_{46}	1	x_{46}	1	0	0	x_{46}	0	0	0	0	1	0
		$\vdots$	$\vdots$	$\vdots$					$\vdots$		$\vdots$			$\vdots$
		y_{80}	1	x_{80}	1	0	0	x_{80}	0	0	0	0	1	0
4.	51 and older	y_{81}	1	x_{81}	1	0	1	x_{81}	0	x_{81}	0	0	0	1
		$\vdots$	$\vdots$	$\vdots$					$\vdots$		$\vdots$			$\vdots$
		y_{100}	1	x_{100}	1	0	1	x_{100}	0	x_{100}	0	0	0	1

Example. We wish to examine the expenditures on furniture by 100 three-person households. First we group these households into four classes according to the age of the head of the household, as shown in Table 6–2. We let y_i and x_i denote the furniture expenditure and income, respectively, of the ith household. The first two columns of the X-matrix in Table 6–2 provide for a simple regression of y on x across all households. Using X_3 in addition to X_1 and X_2 allows us to test the hypothesis that the regression line for the two older groups and the line for the two younger groups have the same intercept by testing the hypothesis that $\beta_3 = 0$. This test can be made with the Student t-variable, as in the preceding section. By introducing both X_4 and X_5, we can find out whether all four groups want different intercepts* by testing $\beta_4 = \beta_5 = 0$. The test of the composite hypothesis, "$\beta_4 = 0$ and $\beta_5 = 0$," cannot be made with the Student t-statistic. However, in this section we shall develop a statistic which can be used for this

---

* When X_1 through X_5 are all in the regression, the intercepts of the four age classes are β_1, $\beta_1 + \beta_4$, $\beta_1 + \beta_3$, and $\beta_1 + \beta_3 + \beta_5$. Note that each one involves an element of β not in the preceding ones, so they are four completely independent values. Exactly the same values of these intercepts and of R^2 and of the coefficient of X_2 would have been obtained if we had used the u_1-, u_2-, u_3-, and u_4-variables, shown at the right of Table 6–2, in place of X_1, X_3, X_4, and X_5. Why?

test. This statistic, known as *Fisher's F*, can be used to test the hypothesis that any number of regression coefficients are zero. In our example, the following tests could also be made:

a) $\beta_3 = \beta_4 = \beta_5 = 0$, the hypothesis that the regression lines of all four groups have the same intercepts (under the assumption that their slopes are all the same),

b) $\beta_6 = 0$, the hypothesis that although the intercepts of all groups are different, the slope in the two younger groups is the same as that in the two older groups,

c) $\beta_6 = \beta_7 = \beta_8 = 0$, the hypothesis that the slopes in all groups are equal.

The result we obtain from using the first five variables (or X_2 and $u_1, \ldots, u_4$) is exactly what we would find if we regressed the deviations from *group* means of the y's on the deviations from *group* mean of the x's. Why? Since the second procedure requires inversion of only a 1-by-1 matrix instead of a 5-by-5 matrix, it is commonly employed. Likewise, the final regression, using eight columns of X, gives a different regression equation for each group of households. These equations are exactly the same as these we would find by doing a regression on each of the four groups separately. Why? Since it is easier to do four regressions with two variables each than to do one regression with eight variables, the separate regressions are usually employed to prepare the total sum of squared residuals which we shall need for the F-statistic.

The test of the equality of intercepts is known as the *analysis of variance*, while the test of the equality of slopes is known as the *analysis of covariance*. Variables such as X_3, X_4, or X_5, which allow the different groups to have different intercepts, are often called *dummy variables*.

Fisher's F-Statistic

Let us now turn to the problem of finding a statistic by which we can test whether the last $n - i$ coefficients of an n-variable regression are all zero:

$$\beta_{i+1} = \beta_{i+2} = \cdots = \beta_n = 0.$$

Let us denote by r_I the vector of residuals when only the first i variables are used, and let us denote by r the vector of residuals when all n variables are used. It then seems reasonable to expect that the quantity

$$u = \frac{r_I' r_I - r' r}{\sigma^2}$$

(where σ^2 is the variance of the e-variable in the equation $y = X\beta + e$) should indicate the significance of the last $n - i$ variables, for this u shows how much variance was explained by the last variables compared to σ^2, the inherent variance in the equation. We know that $r'r/\sigma^2$ is a chi-square variable with $T - n$ degrees of freedom and that under the hypothesis that $\beta_{i+1} = \beta_{i+2} = \cdots = \beta_n = 0$, the variable $r_I'r_I/\sigma^2$ is also chi-square with $T - i$ degrees of freedom.

Theorem 6-13. If in the normal regression $y = X\beta + e$,

$$\beta_{i+1} = \beta_{i+2} = \cdots = \beta_n = 0,$$

then the variable $u = (r_I'r_I - r'r)/\sigma^2$ is the chi-square with $n - i$ degrees of freedom, and is independent of $r'r$.

The strategy for proving this is to express $r_I'r_I$ as the sum of $T - i$ squares of independent normal variables such that the sum of squares of the first $T - n$ of them is $r'r$ and the remaining $n - i$ of them have mean zero, so that $r_I'r_I - r'r$ is the sum of squares of $n - i$ independent normal $(0, \sigma^2)$ variables.

To carry out this plan, however, we need to know the following.

Theorem 6-14 (*Gram-Schmidt orthogonalization*). If $x_1, \ldots, x_n$ are linearly independent vectors, then there exists a set of orthogonal vectors $z_1, \ldots, z_n$ with z_i a linear combination of $x_1, \ldots, x_i$ for $i = 1, \ldots, n$.

Proof. Set $z_1 = x_1/\sqrt{x_1'x_1}$. Proceeding now by induction, we suppose that $z_1, \ldots, z_{i-1}$ have been found. To find z_i we let

$$z_i^* = x_i - \sum_{j=1}^{i-1} (z_j'x_i)z_j.$$

Then for $k < i$, we have

$$z_k'z_i^* = z_k'x_i - z_k'x_i = 0,$$

since $z_k'z_j = 0$ for $i \neq j$, and $z_k'z_k = 1$. Thus, z_i^* is orthogonal to the preceding z-vectors. Dividing it by its length, we get the required z_i of unit length:

$$z_i = z_i^*/\sqrt{z_i^{*\prime}z_i^*}. \qquad \text{Q.E.D.}$$

We can also express this theorem by saying that there exists a triangular matrix W such that

$$Z = XW, \qquad Z'Z = I, \qquad \text{and} \qquad W_{ij} = 0 \qquad \text{if} \quad i > j.$$

Applying the Gauss-Jordan process to the inversion of W, we see immediately that W^{-1} has the same triangularity as W, namely $(W^{-1})_{ij} = 0$ if $i > j$.

Proof of Theorem 6–13. We begin by applying the Gram-Schmidt orthogon-alization to the X-matrix of the given regression equation, $y = X\beta + e$. This equation then becomes $y = Z\beta^* + e$, where $Z = XW$, $Z'Z = I$, $\beta^* = W^{-1}\beta$, and W and W^{-1} are triangular.

Since the first i columns of Z are linear combinations of the first i columns of X, they are equally successful in explaining y by a regression equation. Therefore $r_I'r_I$ is not affected by whether we are working with X or Z.

The least-squares estimate of β^* is

$$b^* = (Z'Z)^{-1}Z'y = Z'y \quad (\text{since } Z'Z = I), \tag{6–4.1}$$

and b^* is normally distributed with variance-covariance matrix equal to

$$\sigma^2(Z'Z)^{-1} = \sigma^2 I. \tag{6–4.2}$$

Now from (6–4.1),

$$r'r = (y' - b^{*\prime}Z')(y - Zb^*) = y'y - 2b^{*\prime}b^* + b^{*\prime}b^* = y'y - b^{*\prime}b^*. \tag{6–4.3}$$

Let us denote the first i columns of Z by Z_I and the first I elements of b^* by b_I^*. Then from (6–4.1),

$$b_I^* = Z_I'y.$$

But

$$(Z_I'Z_I)^{-1}Z_I'y = Z_I'y = b_I^*,$$

so b_I^* is also the regression coefficients of y on Z_I. Therefore, as in (6–4.3),

$$r_I'r_I = y'y - b_I^{*\prime}b_I^*. \tag{6–4.4}$$

Subtracting (6–4.3) from (6–4.4) gives

$$r_I'r_I - r'r = b^{*\prime}b^* - b_I^{*\prime}b_I^*,$$

so

$$u = \frac{b^{*\prime}b^* - b_I^{*\prime}b_I^*}{\sigma^2} = \frac{b_{i+1}^{*2} + \cdots + b_n^{*2}}{\sigma^2}. \tag{6–4.5}$$

But by (6–4.2) the elements of b^*, which are normal and have variances of σ^2, also have zero covariances. Therefore by Theorem 6–10, they are *independent*. It remains only for us to show that the last $n - i$ elements have mean zero.

Now since $\beta^* = W^{-1}\beta$, where all elements of W^{-1} below the diagonal are zero, the last $n - i$ elements of β^* are zero if and only if the last $n - i$ elements of β are zero. Therefore, *under the hypothesis that* $\beta_j = 0$ *for*

$j > i$, $\beta_j^* = 0$ for $j > i$, and, therefore, the $b_{i+1}^*, \ldots, b_n^*$ are independent and normal $(0, \sigma)$. Hence (6–4.5) implies that u is a chi-square variable with $n - i$ degrees of freedom.

Since by Theorem 6–11, r is independent of b^*, $r'r$ is independent of

$$u = \frac{b_{i+1}^{*2} + \cdots + b_n^{*2}}{\sigma^2}. \qquad \text{Q.E.D.}$$

If u is a chi-square variable with p degrees of freedom, v is chi-square with q degrees of freedom, and u and v are independent, then the statistic

$$F = \frac{u/p}{v/q}$$

is called Fisher's F-statistic with (p, q) degrees of freedom. The probability density function of this variable is derived in the appendix to this chapter. Tables of the function can be found in almost any statistical book.

Our Theorem 6–13 establishes that

$$F = \frac{(r_I'r_I - r'r)/\sigma^2(n - i)}{r'r/\sigma^2(T - n)} = \frac{(r_I'r_I - r'r)/(n - i)}{r'r/(T - n)} \qquad (6\text{–}4.6)$$

is a Fisher's F-variable, under the hypothesis that $\beta_{i+1} = \cdots = \beta_n = 0$. It can therefore be used to test the hypothesis just mentioned.

For an example of these tests, we can return to the problem presented in Table 6–2. Let us suppose that the values of $r_I'r_I$ for various values of i are as follows (in thousands):

i	1	2	3	5	6	8
$r_I'r_I$	100	50	47	43	41.5	39

We shall use F_{ij} to denote the F for testing the hypothesis that

$$\beta_{i+1} = \beta_{i+2} = \cdots = \beta_j = 0,$$

while $\beta_1, \ldots, \beta_i$ are allowed to be nonzero.

Values for several of the F's are shown in Table 6–3. The first column of the table shows the degrees-of-freedom pair for each F_{ij}, and the last column shows the 95 percent test level for an F-statistic with those degrees of freedom. For example, an F statistic with $(1, 97)$ degrees of freedom will be less than 3.96 with probability 0.95. From Table 6–3, we see that we can easily reject the hypothesis that the intercepts are equal. The tests of homogeneity of slopes is a bit more interesting. We cannot reject the hypothesis

Table 6–3

SELECTED F-STATISTICS

Degrees of freedom	F	95 percent probability level of F
(1, 97)	$F_{23} = \dfrac{(50 - 47)/1}{47/97} = 6.2$	3.96
(2, 95)	$F_{35} = \dfrac{(47 - 43)/2}{43/95} = 4.4$	3.11
(1, 94)	$F_{56} = \dfrac{(43 - 41.5)/1}{41.5/94} = 3.41$	3.96
(2, 92)	$F_{68} = \dfrac{(41.5 - 39)/2}{39/92} = 2.95$	3.11
(3, 92)	$F_{58} = \dfrac{(43 - 39)/3}{39/92} = 3.15$	2.72

that $\beta_6 = 0$; and, letting β_6 be nonzero, we cannot reject the hypothesis that β_7 and β_8 are both zero. But we *can* reject the hypothesis that β_6, β_7, and β_8 are *all* equal to zero.

The Relation of the F- and t-Statistics

The reader may have noticed that the significance of a single additional variable can be tested by either the Fisher statistic

$$F = \frac{r_I'r_I - r'r}{r'r/(T - n)} = \frac{(b_n^*)^2}{r'r/(T - n)},$$

where $i = n - 1$, or by the Student statistic

$$t = \frac{b_n}{\sqrt{a_{nn}r'r/(T - n)}},$$

where $a_{nn} = (X'X)_{nn}^{-1}$. Now from the definitions of the F- and t-statistics, we see that the square of a t-statistic with $T - n$ degrees of freedom is an F-statistic with $(1, T - n)$ degrees of freedom. To show that, in fact, $t^2 = F$, we need only show that $b_n^2 = a_{nn}b_n^{*2}$, for then

$$t^2 = \frac{b_n^2}{a_{nn}r'r/(T - n)} = \frac{(b_n^*)^2}{r'r/(T - n)} = \frac{r_I'r_I - r'r}{r'r/(T - n)} = F.$$

Since $Wb^* = b$ and W is triangular, $w_{nn}b_n^* = b_n$, so we now have only to show that $w_{nn}^2 = a_{nn}$. Because of the triangularity of W, $(WW')_{nn} = w_{nn}^2$.

Therefore we need only show that $WW' = (X'X)^{-1}$. But

$$W'X'XW = Z'Z = I,$$

so

$$X'X = (W')^{-1}W^{-1}$$

or

$$WW' = (X'X)^{-1}.$$

The proof that $F = t^2$ is therefore complete; hence the two tests always yield identical answers.

PROBLEMS

1. In a sample of 62 steam plants built between 1947 and 1965, fuel consumption was regressed on electrical generation and a constant term. When all plants were put into one regression, the sum of squared residuals was 144. When the plants were divided into three groups by age and each group was allowed to have its own intercept, the sum of squared residuals fell to 130. When separate regressions were run on each group, the sum of the squares of all residuals was 120. What do you conclude about the nature of technological change in steam generation plants over the period during which these plants were built?

2. A regression with six independent variables was first fitted to 48 quarterly observations of new housing starts. The resulting sum of squared residuals was 108. A year later, the same equation was fitted to 52 observations and the sum of squared residuals rose to 120. At the 95 percent level, would you reject the hypothesis that the structure was the same in the last year as in previous years? [*Hint:* Interpret the sum of squared residuals for the 48 quarters as the result of a 52-quarter regression with four additional dummy variables to provide a special intercept for each of the last four quarters. The hypothesis of homogeneity is that the coefficients of these dummies are all zero.]

APPENDIX

PROBABILITY DISTRIBUTIONS CONNECTED WITH THE NORMAL

The Chi-Square Distribution

Theorem 1. If $v^2 = x'x$, where x is a vector of n independent variables, all normal $(0, 1)$, then the probability density function of v is

$$f(v) = c_n e^{-v^2/2} v^{n-1}, \tag{1}$$

where c_n is a constant such that $\int_{-\infty}^{\infty} f(z)\, dz = 1$.

Proof. The joint density function of the x-variables is $ce^{-x'x/2}$. Let us consider first the case in which $n = 2$. Then in Fig. 6–6, everywhere on a circle of radius r, the following are true:

a) $v = \sqrt{x'x}$ has the same value, namely r, and

b) the joint probability density of the x's is constant and equal to $ce^{-r^2/2}$.

Therefore, the differential approximation of the probability of v falling between r and $r + dr$ is

$$f(v)\, dv = ce^{-r^2/2} \quad \text{(circumference of a circle of radius } r) \, dr$$
$$= 2\pi ce^{-r^2/2} r\, dr = c_2 e^{-v^2/2} v\, dv,$$

where $v = r$, $dv = dr$, and dr is small. Analogously, for the case $n > 2$, we have

$$f(v) = ce^{-r^2/2} \quad \text{(surface area of an } n\text{-dimensional sphere of radius } r)$$
$$= c_n e^{-r^2/2} r^{n-1} = c_n e^{-v^2/2} v^{n-1}.$$
$$\text{Q.E.D.}$$

It is not v, however, but v^2 which is the chi-square variable. If we let $u = v^2$, $du = 2v\, dv$, the substitution shows that the density function of u is

$$c_n e^{-v^2/2} v^{n-1}\, dv = \tfrac{1}{2} c_n e^{-v^2/2} v^{n-2}(2v\, dv)$$
$$= \tfrac{1}{2} c_n e^{-u/2} u^{(n-2)/2}\, du.$$

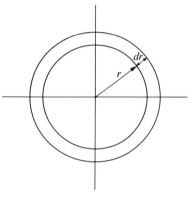

Figure 6–6

The Student *t*-Distribution

Theorem 2. If u is normal $(0, 1)$, v^2 has chi-square distribution with n degrees of freedom, and u and v are independent, then

$$t = \frac{u}{\sqrt{v^2/n}}$$

has the density function

$$f(t) = c(1 + t^2/n)^{-(n+1)/2}.$$

Proof. By Eq. (1) the density function of v is

$$g(v) = cv^{n-1} e^{-v^2/2}.$$

Here and subsequently, c denotes any constant of no immediate interest, and, therefore, *the value of c may be different in different equations.*

Since u and v are independent, their joint density function is

$$f(u, v) = ce^{-u^2/2}v^{n-1}e^{-v^2/2} = cv^{n-1}e^{-(u^2+v^2)/2}.$$

Let us fix v and replace u by $u = tv/\sqrt{n}$. By the substitution rule, the joint density of v and t is

$$g(t, v) = cv^n e^{-(v^2+t^2v^2/n)/2}.$$

But the density of t is

$$f(t) = \int_0^\infty g(t, v)\, dv = c \int_0^\infty v^n e^{-(v^2/2)(1+t^2/n)}\, dv.$$

Let $y = (v^2/2)(1 + t^2/n)$. Then $dy = v(1 + t^2/n)\, dv$, and

$$f(t) = c \int_0^\infty \left(\frac{2y}{1 + t^2/n}\right)^{n/2} e^{-y} \left(\frac{2y}{1 + t^2/n}\right)^{-1/2} \left(\frac{dy}{1 + t^2/n}\right)$$

$$= c\left(1 + \frac{t^2}{n}\right)^{-(n+1)/2} \int_0^\infty y^{(n-1)/2}e^{-y}\, dy$$

$$= c\left(1 + \frac{t^2}{n}\right)^{-(n+1)/2},$$

since the integral in the next to the last line is a constant.   Q.E.D.

Fisher's *F*-Distribution

Theorem 3. If u and v are independent chi-square variables with m and n degrees of freedom, respectively, then the density function of $F = (u/m)/(v/n)$ is

$$f(F) = cF^{m/2-1}(n + mF)^{-(m+n)/2}.$$

Proof. The joint density function of u and v is

$$f(u, v) = cu^{m/2-1}v^{n/2-1}e^{-(1/2)(u+v)}.$$

We introduce F by the change of variable $u = Fvm/n$, $du = (vm/n)\, dF$. Then from the substitution rule, we find that the joint density function of F and v is

$$g(F, v) = F^{m/2-1} v^{(m+n)/2-1} e^{-(v/2)(Fm/n+1)}.$$

Therefore

$$f(F) = \int_0^\infty g(F, v)\, dv = c \int_0^\infty F^{m/2-1} v^{(m+n)/2-1} e^{-(v/2)(Fm/n+1)}\, dv.$$

Substituting for v with

$$y = (v/2)(Fm/n + 1), \qquad dy = \tfrac{1}{2}(Fm/n + 1)\, dv,$$

we obtain

$$f(F) = cF^{m/2-1} \int_0^\infty \left(\frac{2y}{Fm/n + 1}\right)^{(m+n)/2-1} e^{-y} \frac{2\, dy}{Fm/n + 1}$$

$$= cF^{m/n-1}(Fm/n + 1)^{-(m+n)/2} \int_0^\infty y^{(m+n)/2-1} e^{-y}\, dy$$

$$= cF^{m/n-1}(n + mF)^{-(m+n)/2}. \quad \text{Q.E.D.}$$

CHAPTER 7

CHARACTERISTIC VALUES OF
NONSYMMETRIC MATRICES

7–1 LINEAR DIFFERENTIAL EQUATIONS
AND CHARACTERISTIC POLYNOMIALS

As we studied the characteristic values and vectors of symmetric matrices, the reader may have wondered whether the solutions of the equation $Ax = \lambda x$ have any applications when A is *not* symmetric. Indeed they do, but because the solutions are far harder to calculate (except when A is 2 by 2), their use is confined to theoretical results even more than in the symmetric case.

The most instructive use of characteristic values of nonsymmetric matrices lies in systems of simultaneous linear differential equations. Let $x(t)$ be a vector of functions of the variable t (which is usually "time"), and let $\dot{x}(t)$ be the vector of derivatives of these functions with respect to t. The equation

$$\dot{x}(t) = Ax(t), \tag{7–1.1}$$

where A is a square matrix, is a system of simultaneous differential equations. Such systems arise in the study of business cycles or economic growth. A vector $x(t)$ of functions which satisfies Eq. (7–1.1) is said to be a solution of the equations.

We usually do not want just any solution of Eq. (7–1.1), but only the one passing through some given initial point, $x(0) = x^0$. Now the simplest way to calculate such a solution is to increase t by small steps, $0, t_1, t_2, t_3, \ldots$, and to calculate

$$
\begin{aligned}
x(t_1) &= x(0) + Ax^0(t_1 - 0), \\
x(t_2) &= x(t_1) + Ax(t_1)(t_2 - t_1), \\
&\vdots \\
x(t_i) &= x(t_{i-1}) + Ax(t_{i-1})(t_i - t_{i-1}).
\end{aligned}
\tag{7–1.2}
$$

143

These calculations are clearly easy to program for a computer, and by taking the increments in t small enough, they can be made to give as accurate a solution of (7–1.1) as desired. Offhand, however, Eqs. (7–1.2) do not tell us much about the solution, whether it will show steady fluctuations, irregular jerks, or just what. It is here, in showing the character of the solution, that the theory of characteristic roots is revealing.

We know that a solution of the single equation

$$\dot{x} = ax$$

is $x = ce^{at}$, where c is any constant. Can this solution be generalized? Can we find a scalar λ and a vector v such that $x(t) = ve^{\lambda t}$? For this $x(t)$, $\dot{x}(t) = \lambda v e^{\lambda t}$, and substituting into (7–1.1), we get

$$\lambda v e^{\lambda t} = A v e^{\lambda t}$$

or

$$\lambda v = Av. \tag{7–1.3}$$

In other words, $x(t) = ve^{\lambda t}$ is a solution of (7–1.1) if and only if v is a characteristic vector and λ is the characteristic value of A corresponding to v.

If $x(t)$ and $y(t)$ are two solutions of (7–1.1), it can easily be verified that $c_1 x(t) + c_2 y(t)$ is also a solution for any values of the constants c_1 and c_2.

If, therefore, A *were* symmetric and V were the matrix of its orthogonal characteristic vectors, then

$$x(t) = \sum_{i=1}^{n} c_i V_i e^{\lambda_i t} \tag{7–1.4}$$

would be a solution for any values of the c's. In particular, if we choose the c-vector so that

$$Vc = x^0, \tag{7–1.5}$$

then the solution, Eq. (7–1.4), passes through the desired initial point. Since Eqs. (7–1.2) make it pretty clear that there is only one solution passing through that initial point, we see that *all* solutions are of the form (7–1.4). That is, all solutions are the sum of n exponential functions, a fact which reveals a good deal about what the solutions can look like.

But if A is not symmetric, then what? Will there be any characteristic values of A? Will there be n of them? Will the characteristic vectors be independent so that Eq. (7–1.5) can be solved? The answer to all of these questions is a qualified "yes." Let us begin with the first: will there be any characteristic values of A? There will be if and only if $x(t) = ve^{\lambda t}$ is a solution of

$$\dot{x} = Ax. \tag{7–1.1'}$$

Let us see what conditions these equations place on the first component of the x-vector, $x_1(t)$, and its derivatives. We shall use $\dot{x}_1$ to replace x_2 in (7–1.1), then $\ddot{x}_1$ to replace x_3, and so on, until we have an equation involving only x_1 and its derivatives. We can then easily find the necessary and sufficient condition λ for $x_1(t) = v_1 e^{\lambda t}$ to be its solution.

To eliminate x_2, we use the first equation to express x_2 in terms of $\dot{x}_1$, $x_1, x_3, \ldots, x_n$ and then eliminate x_2 from the other equations, thus obtaining

$$
\begin{pmatrix} \dot{x}_1 \\ \dot{x}_2 \\ \vdots \\ \dot{x}_n \end{pmatrix} = \begin{pmatrix} 0 & 1 & 0 & \cdots & 0 \\ a_{21} - \dfrac{a_{22}a_{11}}{a_{12}} & \dfrac{a_{22}}{a_{12}} & a_{23} - \dfrac{a_{22}a_{13}}{a_{12}} \cdots a_{2n} - \dfrac{a_{22}a_{1n}}{a_{12}} \\ \vdots & \vdots & & \vdots \\ a_{n1} - \dfrac{a_{n2}a_{11}}{a_{12}} & \dfrac{a_{n2}}{a_{12}} & a_{n3} - \dfrac{a_{n3}a_{13}}{a_{12}} \cdots a_{nn} - \dfrac{a_{n2}a_{1n}}{a_{12}} \end{pmatrix} \begin{pmatrix} x_1 \\ \dot{x}_1 \\ x_3 \\ \vdots \\ x_n \end{pmatrix}.
$$

(7–1.6)

Note that we determine the matrix on the right-hand side of Eq. (7–1.6), the matrix which we shall call B, from A by pivoting by columns on a_{12}, rather than by rows, as in the Gauss-Jordan process. We may also think of B as being the result of the postmultiplication of A by the matrix

$$
M_2 = \begin{pmatrix} 1 & 0 & 0 & \cdots & 0 \\ -a_{11}/a_{12} & 1/a_{12} & -a_{13}/a_{12} \cdots & -a_{1n}/a_{12} \\ 0 & 0 & 1 & \cdots & 0 \\ \vdots & & & & \vdots \\ 0 & 0 & 0 & \cdots & 1 \end{pmatrix}.
$$

(7–1.7)

Thus, $B = AM_2$.

To continue the process of replacing $x_2, \ldots, x_n$ by $\dot{x}_1, \ldots, x_1^{(n-1)}$, we need an equation for $\ddot{x}_1$ which involves only those variables on the right-hand side of (7–1.6). By differentiating the first equation of (7–1.1), we see that we can find such an expression for $\ddot{x}_1$ by adding together the equations in (7–1.6) with the weights $a_{11}, a_{12}, \ldots, a_{1n}$, respectively. Replacing the second equation of (7–1.6) by this equation for $\ddot{x}_1$, we get a system without x_2 or its derivatives, namely

$$
\begin{pmatrix} \dot{x}_1 \\ \ddot{x}_1 \\ \dot{x}_3 \\ \vdots \\ \dot{x}_n \end{pmatrix} = C_2 \begin{pmatrix} x_1 \\ \dot{x}_1 \\ x_3 \\ \vdots \\ x_n \end{pmatrix},
$$

(7–1.8)

where C_2 is the matrix obtained by premultiplying B by

$$N_2 = \begin{pmatrix} 1 & 0 & 0 \cdots 0 \\ a_{11} & a_{12} & a_{13} \cdots a_{1n} \\ 0 & 0 & 1 \cdots 0 \\ \vdots & & \vdots \\ 0 & 0 & 0 \cdots 1 \end{pmatrix}; \qquad (7\text{--}1.9)$$

that is, $C_2 = N_2B = N_2AM_2$. Note that the matrices C_2 and B are identical except in the second row. For future reference, we may note now that $N_2 = M_2^{-1}$.

Now (7–1.8) is of the same form as (7–1.1): the vector on the left-hand side is the derivative of the vector on the right. We can therefore repeat the process to eliminate x_3 and $\dot{x}_3$ by introducing $\ddot{x}_1$ on the right and $\dddot{x}_1$ on the left. The procedure is repeated until we have the equations

$$\begin{pmatrix} \dot{x}_1 \\ \ddot{x}_1 \\ \vdots \\ x_1^{(n)} \end{pmatrix} = \begin{pmatrix} 0 & 1 & 0 \cdots & 0 \\ 0 & 0 & 1 \cdots & 0 \\ \vdots & & & \vdots \\ 0 & 0 & 0 \cdots & 1 \\ -c_0 & -c_1 & -c_2 \cdots & -c_{n-1} \end{pmatrix} \begin{pmatrix} x_1 \\ \dot{x}_1 \\ \vdots \\ x_1^{(n-1)} \end{pmatrix}. \qquad (7\text{--}1.10)$$

A matrix of the form shown on the right of (7–1.10) is called a Frobenius matrix. This method of getting A in Frobenius form is called the Danilevsky process. From the last equation of (7–1.10) we read

$$x_1^{(n)} = -[c_0x_1 + c_1\dot{x}_1 + c_2\ddot{x} + \cdots + c_{n-1}x^{(n-1)}]. \qquad (7\text{--}1.11)$$

The function $x_1(t) = v_1e^{\lambda t}$ is a solution of (7–1.11) if and only if

$$P(\lambda) = \lambda^n + c_{n-1}\lambda^{n-1} + \cdots + c_1\lambda + c_0 = 0, \qquad (7\text{--}1.12)$$

as is easily seen when we substitute it into (7–1.11) and cancel $e^{\lambda t}$ from both sides. Hence, if λ is a characteristic value of A, it must be a root of the polynomial given in (7–1.12). Conversely, if λ *is* a root of (7–1.12), then $x_1(t) = e^{\lambda t}$ satisfies (7–1.10), and, by defining $x_n, x_{n-1}, \ldots, x_2$ by the equations used to eliminate them in deriving (7–1.9) from (7–1.1), we find that each of them has the form $x_i(t) = v_ie^{\lambda t}$ and that they satisfy Eq. (7–1.1). Therefore, if λ is a root of the polynomial (7–1.12), it is a characteristic value of A. It is natural, therefore, to call (7–1.12) the characteristic polynomial of A, and we can easily remember the following theorem.

Theorem 7–1. λ is a characteristic value of A if and only if it is a root of the characteristic polynomial of A.

Our demonstration of this theorem has relied upon the connection between characteristic values and differential equations. Since the theorem itself makes no reference to differential equations, it should be possible to prove it without them. In the next section, we shall give a short and simple proof of this sort; it comes, however, directly out of our above discussion and was surely discovered by somebody working with differential equations.

Theorem 7–1 allows us to apply to characteristic values all the theorems about the roots of polynomials. We cannot go into the proofs here, but from almost any college algebra book one can learn the following:

a) An nth degree polynomial [such as (7–1.12)] has n roots. In general, these roots are distinct; if they are not, a slight change in coefficients will make them distinct.
b) Some or all of the roots may be complex, that is, they may be of the form $a + bi$, where a and b are real numbers and $i^2 = -1$.
c) Complex roots occur in conjugate pairs. If $\lambda = a + bi$ is a root, so is $\lambda^* = a - bi$.
d) The polynomial can be factored and written

$$P(\lambda) = (\lambda - \lambda_1)(\lambda - \lambda_2) \cdots (\lambda - \lambda_n),$$

where $\lambda_1, \ldots, \lambda_n$ are the roots of $P(\lambda)$.

For applications in differential equations, the following theorem is important.

Theorem 7–2. If $\lambda_1, \ldots, \lambda_k$ are k *distinct* characteristic values of a matrix A, and $V_1, \ldots, V_k$ are associated characteristic vectors, then the $V_1, \ldots, V_k$ are linearly independent.

Proof. If the $V_1, \ldots, V_k$ are linearly dependent, then one, say V_{r+1}, is a linear combination of linearly independent ones, say $V_1, \ldots, V_r$; that is, there exists $c_1, \ldots, c_r$ not all equal to zero such that

$$V_{r+1} = \sum_{j=1}^{r} c_j V_j. \tag{7-1.13}$$

Multiplying both sides of (7–1.13) by A gives

$$\lambda_{r+1} V_{r+1} = \sum_{j=1}^{r} c_j \lambda_j V_j. \tag{7-1.14}$$

Multiplying (7–1.13) by λ_{r+1} and substituting from (7–1.14) yields

$$0 = \sum_{j=1}^{r} a_j(\lambda_j - \lambda_{r+1}) V_j. \tag{7-1.15}$$

But since $(\lambda_j - \lambda_{r+1}) \neq 0$, Eq. (7-1.15) contradicts the fact that the $V_1, \ldots, V_r$ are linearly independent. Therefore, the assumption that the $V_1, \ldots, V_k$ are linearly dependent cannot be maintained, and the theorem is proved.

By virtue of this theorem, if the characteristic values of A are all distinct, as they generally will be, all solutions of the differential equation (7-1.1) can be written as

$$x(t) = \sum_{i=1}^{n} c_i V_i e^{\lambda_i t} \qquad (7\text{-}1.16)$$

just as in the case of a symmetric A, as shown in (7-1.4). The only difference between Eqs. (7-1.4) and (7-1.16) is that in (7-1.4), c_i, V_i, and λ_i were all real, while in (7-1.16), some or all may be complex.

From the back pages of most calculus books, we can learn that when $\lambda = a + bi$ is complex,

$$e^{\lambda t} = e^{(a+bi)t} = e^{at}e^{ibt} = e^{at} (\cos bt + i \sin bt).$$

(Here e^{ib} is defined as $\cos b + i \sin b$, because we wish that

$$\frac{d}{db} e^{ib} = ie^{ib}.$$

This definition, and only this definition, has this property.) The sine and cosine terms provide oscillations in the solution. If the real part of the root, a, is positive, the amplitude of these oscillations grows, whereas if a is negative, the amplitude is damped. The system of equations is therefore said to be *stable* if all the roots have negative real parts. Sometimes we can prove the stability or instability of a system *a priori*. If not, we can calculate the characteristic polynomial and apply the test given in the appendix to this chapter. Calculating the roots themselves, especially the complex roots, of a polynomial of high degree—say involving λ^5 or higher powers—is a task one does well to avoid. Methods are described in numerical analysis books, but the best of them are difficult and imperfect. It must be emphasized that solutions of systems of differential equations with more than two or three variables should not be approached through characteristic values. Because of the criterion given in the appendix and the relative ease of computing the characteristic equation by the Danilevsky process, this approach is useful for the study of stability and the closely related subject of the sensitivity of the system of random inputs.

Since most algebra books use determinants rather than the Danilevsky process to find the characteristic polynomial, it is perhaps worth pointing out that for matrices larger than 3 by 3, the Danilevsky method is far more efficient. For example, for a 9-by-9 matrix, the use of determinants takes about one and one-half thousand times as much work as the Danilevsky method.

PROBLEMS

1. Use the Danilevsky method to find the characteristic equation of the following matrix:

$$A = \begin{pmatrix} 32 & -1 & -4 \\ -12 & 4 & 48 \\ 19 & -1 & -4 \end{pmatrix}.$$

2. Write a FORTRAN program to perform the Danilevsky process. Have the program also calculate $M = M_2 M_3 \cdots M_n$.

7–2 SIMILAR MATRICES

In this section we give a pure algebraic proof of Theorem 7–1. We need first the following definition: A matrix A is said to be *similar* to a matrix B if there exists a nonsingular matrix M such that $A = MBM^{-1}$.

If A is similar to B, then B is similar to A, for

$$B = M^{-1}AM = (M^{-1})A(M^{-1})^{-1},$$

where M^{-1} is, of course, a nonsingular matrix.

The following theorem shows the close connection between the study of characteristic values and that of similar matrices.

Theorem 7–3. Similar matrices have the same characteristic values.

Proof. Suppose that

a) λ is a characteristic value of B, that is, that there exists a v such that $Bv = \lambda v$, and

b) $A = MBM^{-1}$. Then

$$A(Mv) = MBM^{-1}(Mv) = MBv = M(\lambda v) = \lambda(Mv),$$

so that λ is a characteristic value of A also, with Mv as an associated characteristic vector.

In the preceding section, we noted that the M_2 and N_2 of Eqs. (7–1.7) and (7–1.9) are inverses. By defining $N_3, N_4, \ldots, N_n$ in a manner analogous to the way in which we defined N_2, we see that the Frobenius matrix F in

Eq. (7–1.10) is

$$F = N_n N_{n-1} \cdots N_2 A N_2^{-1} N_3^{-1} \cdots N_n^{-1}.$$

Since $(N_2^{-1} \cdots N_n^{-1}) = (N_n \cdots N_2)^{-1}$, F is similar to A, and therefore, by Theorem 7–1, has the same charateristic values as A. If λ is a root of the equation

$$\lambda^n + c_{n-1}\lambda^{n-1} + \cdots + c_1\lambda + c_0 = 0, \tag{7–2.1}$$

then λ is a characteristic value of F, for $(1, \lambda, \lambda^2, \ldots, \lambda^{n-1})'$ is a characteristic vector with the characteristic value λ:

$$\begin{pmatrix} 0 & 1 & 0 & \cdots & 0 \\ 0 & 0 & 1 & \cdots & 0 \\ \vdots & & & & \vdots \\ 0 & 0 & 0 & \cdots & 1 \\ -c_0 & -c_1 & -c_2 & \cdots & -c_{n-1} \end{pmatrix} \begin{pmatrix} 1 \\ \lambda \\ \vdots \\ \lambda^{n-2} \\ \lambda^{n-1} \end{pmatrix} = \begin{pmatrix} \lambda \\ \lambda^2 \\ \vdots \\ \lambda^{n-1} \\ \lambda^n \end{pmatrix} = \lambda \begin{pmatrix} 1 \\ \lambda \\ \vdots \\ \lambda^{n-2} \\ \lambda^{n-1} \end{pmatrix}. \tag{7–2.2}$$

Conversely, if λ is a characteristic value of F, it will clearly have to satisfy Eq. (7–2.1), for if we pick $v_1 = 1$ or any other constant, the first $n - 1$ equations of $Fv = \lambda v$ completely determine v, and the nth equation will then be satisfied only if λ is a root of the polynomial (7–2.1). Therefore, we have again proved

Theorem 7–4. λ is a characteristic value of A if and only if it is a root of the characteristic polynomial.

Similarity of matrices has a clear geometrical interpretation, namely,

Theorem 7–5. If A and B are similar, they represent the same transformation of space relative to different bases.

Proof. Let $A = MBM^{-1}$, and let P^0 be a point in space. Relative to the coordinate vectors $e_1, \ldots, e_n$, let us say that P^0 is represented by the vector x; but relative to the vectors represented (relative to $e_1, \ldots, e_n$) by the columns of M, the same P^0 is represented by y, defined by $x = My$. Now let us multiply x by A to get $u = Ax$, the representation, relative to $e_1, \ldots, e_n$, of the point P^1 into which P^0 has been transformed. Let us next transform y by B to get $z = By = BM^{-1}x$. This z represents, relative to the columns of M, some point P^2. The theorem asserts that P^1 and P^2 are the same point. To prove that they are, we need only show that they both have the same representation relative to $e_1, \ldots, e_n$. For P^2, this representation is $v = Mz$; for P^1, it is $u = Ax$. But

$$v = Mz = MBy = MBM^{-1}x = Ax = u,$$

and the proof is complete.

By combining Theorems 7–3 and 7–5, we obtain at once

Theorem 7–6. Two different matrices represent the same transformation relative to two different bases if and only if they have the same characteristic values.

This theorem, perhaps more than all others, justifies the adjective "characteristic" for these values. They are the soul of the matrix, its character. Through all the incarnations a matrix undergoes to work upon the many representations of space, they alone survive and determine how the matrix transforms its world.

PROBLEMS

1. Show that two matrices are similar if we derive one from the other by interchanging two rows and then interchanging the two corresponding columns.
2. Our proofs have assumed that in the Danilevsky method a zero was never found in the pivot position. Show how such a zero can be handled if it appears.
3. Find the roots of the characteristic polynomial found in Problem 1 of Section 7–1. Find the characteristic vectors of the Frobenius matrix, and transform them (see Theorem 7–3) into the characteristic vectors of the given A-matrix.
4. (*Cayley-Hamilton theorem.*) Every matrix satisfies its own characteristic polynomial; that is,

$$A^n + c_{n-1}A^{n-1} + \cdots + c_1 A + c^0 = 0,$$

where the 0 represents a square matrix of zeros. Prove this theorem for the case where A has n distinct roots. [*Hint:* Postmultiply the expression on the left-hand side of the above equation by a characteristic vector of A, and note that the result is a zero vector.]

APPENDIX

A SIMPLE TEST FOR STABILITY

Since the question of whether or not a system is stable may be crucial to its economic interpretation, it is fortunate that stability can be determined much more easily than all of the complex roots can be computed.   This determination can be done by the following theorem.   An understanding of its proof may require a reading of the first dozen pages of a book on complex variables.

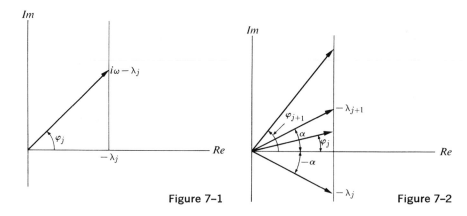

Figure 7–1

Figure 7–2

Theorem 1. All roots of the nth degree polynomial $P(\lambda)$ have negative real parts if and only if the graph (in the complex plane) of $P(i\omega)$ makes n counterclockwise quarter-turns around the origin as ω goes from zero to infinity. (By a quarter-turn, we mean $\pi/2$ radians.)

Proof. If $\lambda_1, \ldots, \lambda_n$ are the roots of $P(\lambda)$, then

$$P(\lambda) = (\lambda - \lambda_1) \cdots (\lambda - \lambda_n)$$

or, writing $i\omega - \lambda_j$ in exponential form, $i\omega - \lambda_j = r_j e^{i\varphi_j}$, we have

$$P(i\omega) = r_1 e^{i\varphi_1} \cdots r_n e^{i\varphi_n} = r_1 \cdots r_n e^{i(\varphi_1 + \cdots + \varphi_n)}.$$

Thus the argument of $P(i\omega)$ is the sum of the arguments of the $(i\omega - \lambda_j)$, and therefore the total increment as $\omega \to \infty$ in the former is the sum of the increments in the latter.

Now if λ_j is a negative real root, then from Fig. 7–1 we see that as ω goes from 0 to ∞, the line connecting $i\omega - \lambda_j$ and the origin makes a quarter-turn counterclockwise. If λ_j and λ_{j+1} are a pair of complex roots with negative real parts and disposed as shown in Fig. 7–2, then as $\omega \to \infty$, φ_j goes from $-\alpha$ to $\pi/2$ and φ_{j+1} goes from α to $\pi/2$, so that the combined increment in the two angles is π, or two quarter-turns. Thus, *if $P(\lambda)$ has n roots with negative real parts, $P(i\omega)$ makes n quarter-turns around the origin as ω goes from 0 to ∞.* Exactly similar reasoning shows that for each root with a positive real part, there is a quarter-turn in the clockwise direction; consequently, the $P(i\omega)$ can make n quarter-turns counterclockwise *only if* all roots have negative real parts. Q.E.D.

SUPPLEMENTARY READINGS

Chapter 1

Gantmacher, F.R., *The Theory of Matrices*, Interscience, New York, 1959. A comprehensive treatise on matrices; a clear exposition written from a practical point of view.

Miernyk, William H., *The Elements of Input-Output Analysis*, Random House, New York, 1965. A careful exposition of this subject with good references for further reading.

Chapter 2

Hoel, Paul G., *Introduction to Mathematical Statistics*, John Wiley and Sons, Inc., New York, 1954. See the early chapters for the basic ideas in statistics.

Johnston, J., *Econometric Methods*, McGraw-Hill, New York, 1963. See pp. 106–116 for discussion of the "best linear unbiased estimate" properties.

Chapter 3

In addition to the reference manuals put out by the computer manufacturers, the following work is valuable because of its integration of mathematical explanation and programming. It contains a number of complete programs for study.

McCormich, John M., and Mario G. Salvadori, *Numerical Methods in FORTRAN*, Prentice-Hall, Englewood Cliffs, N.J., 1964.

Chapter 4

Dantzig, George B., *Linear Programming and Extensions*, Princeton University Press, Princeton, 1963. A masterly book by the inventor of the simplex method. It contains a wealth of material on special methods which are useful for particular problems.

Driebeek, Norman, "An Algorithm for the Solution of Mixed Integer Programming Problems," *Management Science*, March 1966.

Naylor, Thomas H., and Eugene T. Bryne, *Linear Programming; Methods and Cases*, Wadsworth, Belmont, Calif., 1963. The cases are particularly worth reading.

Chapter 5

Boot, John C. G., *Quadratic Programming*, Rand McNally, New York, 1964. A very clear exposition of an interesting application of the Kuhn-Tucker theorem and the simplex method to problems with quadratic objective functions.

Crowell, R. H., and R. E. Williamson, *Calculus of Vector Functions*, Prentice-Hall, Englewood Cliffs, N.J., 1962. A treatment of the calculus of several variables written in a spirit akin to this book.

Fan, L. T., and C. S. Wang, *The Discrete Maximum Principle*, John Wiley, New York, 1963.

Pontryagin, L. S., et al., *The Mathematical Theory of Optimal Processes*, Interscience, New York, 1962.

Chapter 6

Johnston, J., *Econometric Methods*, McGraw-Hill, New York, 1963.

Chapter 7

Kaplan, Wilfred, *Ordinary Differential Equations*, Addison-Wesley, Reading, Mass., 1964, especially the appendix to Chapter 6. This book is one of the few texts which explain differential equations in a manner appropriate for students of economics.

APPENDIX ON DETERMINANTS

Determinants have received attention in textbooks and a prominence in economic writing out of all proportion to their intrinsic usefulness. The impression is often given that we must calculate determinants in order to invert a matrix, test the positive definiteness of a matrix, or find the characteristic polynomial of a matrix. In fact, determinants are of no computational —or, as far as I can see, theoretical—value in any of these connections. Nevertheless, because it is necessary to know a few things about determinants to read articles which antedate the realization of the superiority of inverse-matrix and partitioned-matrix notation, the rudiments of the subject will be given here.

The determinant $|A|$ of a square matrix A can be defined in a number of equivalent ways; the definition we use here is perhaps the simplest of all, namely $|A|$ is the *product of the pivot elements* in the Gauss-Jordan inversion of A. (If it is necessary to interchange rows in the course of the inversion, the product is multiplied by a -1 for each such interchange.) For a 2-by-2 determinant, therefore,

$$\begin{vmatrix} a & b \\ c & d \end{vmatrix} = a\left(d - c\frac{b}{a}\right) = ad - bc. \tag{1}$$

This definition makes the following theorem completely obvious.

Theorem 1. $|A| = 0$ if and only if A is singular.

This definition of the determinant is also the form in which it naturally arises in the transformation of multiple integrals; see Section 6–3 and the change of variable technique.

Theorem 2. $|A| = |A'|$.

155

Proof. The proof is by mathematical induction. When A is 2 by 2, the theorem can be verified directly from Eq. (1). Let us assume that it is true for $(n-1)$-dimensional matrices and prove it for n-dimensional ones. Let

$$A = \begin{pmatrix} a_{11} & A_{12} \\ A_{21} & A_{22} \end{pmatrix}$$

be n by n and A_{22}, $(n-1)$ by $(n-1)$. Then

$$|A| = a_{11} \cdot |A_{22} - A_{21}A_{12}a_{11}^{-1}|,$$

while

$$|A'| = a_{11} \cdot |A'_{22} - A'_{12}A'_{21}a_{11}^{-1}|,$$

but the second terms on the right-hand side are equal by the induction hypothesis; the matrices involved are $(n-1)$ by $(n-1)$, and one is the transpose of the other. Therefore $|A| = |A'|$ and the theorem is proved.

Theorem 3. Interchanging two rows or two columns of a matrix changes the sign but not the absolute value of its determinant.

Proof. We may confine our discussion to the interchange of two rows, for Theorem 2 can be used to establish for columns anything which is true for rows. From Eq. (1), the theorem can be established for 2-by-2 matrices. Let us therefore assume that it holds for a matrix with dimension *less* than n and prove that it holds for those of dimension n. Let A be the original matrix, and let B be the matrix after the interchange. Three cases may be distinguished.

CASE I. The last two rows are interchanged. Let us partition the matrices

$$A = \begin{pmatrix} A_{11} & A_{12} \\ A_{21} & A_{22} \end{pmatrix}, \qquad B = \begin{pmatrix} A_{11} & A_{12} \\ B_{21} & B_{22} \end{pmatrix},$$

where A_{22} and B_{22} are 2 by 2; the two rows of $(A_{21}A_{22})$ and $(B_{21}B_{22})$ are interchanged. Now, by the definition,

$$|A| = |A_{11}| \cdot |A_{22} - A_{21}A_{11}^{-1}A_{12}|$$

and

$$|B| = |A_{11}| \cdot |B_{22} - B_{21}A_{11}^{-1}A_{12}|.$$

But the matrices in the second determinant on the right-hand side of these two equations are 2 by 2, and are the same except that their rows have been interchanged. Therefore, by the induction hypothesis, one is the negative of the other and

$$|A| = -|B|.$$

CASE II.   Two of the first $n-1$ rows are interchanged.   We partition as follows:

$$A = \begin{pmatrix} A_{11} & A_{12} \\ A_{21} & A_{22} \end{pmatrix}, \qquad B = \begin{pmatrix} B_{11} & B_{12} \\ A_{21} & A_{22} \end{pmatrix},$$

where A_{22} is 1 by 1.   Then, by the definition, as before

$$|A| = |A_{11}| \cdot |A_{22} - A_{21}A_{11}^{-1}A_{12}|,$$
$$|B| = |B_{11}| \cdot |A_{22} - A_{21}B_{11}^{-1}B_{12}|.$$

Now by the induction hypothesis, $|A_{11}| = -|B_{11}|$.   Since interchanging two rows of a matrix interchanges the two corresponding columns of the inverse, $A_{11}^{-1}A_{12} = B_{11}^{-1}B_{12}$, and the second determinants on the right of the two equations are equal.   Therefore $|A| = -|B|$.

CASE III.   The last and one of the first $n-1$ (other than the next to last) rows are interchanged.   This case is reducible to the first two.   Suppose that rows m and n have been interchanged.   We could accomplish this interchange by interchanging row m and row $n-1$ (one change of sign), then interchanging rows n and $n-1$ (second change of sign), and then interchanging $n-1$ and m again (the third change of sign).   Since $(-1)^3 = -1$, again $|A| = -|B|$, and the theorem is proved.

From Theorem 3, we can see that the product of the pivot elements obtained by the usual inversion process is the same as the product we would obtain if we started pivoting in the lower right-hand corner of the matrix and worked our way back up and to the left-hand corner.   This fact gives rise to

Theorem 4 (*Jacobi's Theorem*).   Let

$$A^{-1} = \begin{pmatrix} A_{11} & A_{12} \\ A_{21} & A_{22} \end{pmatrix}^{-1} = \begin{pmatrix} A^{11} & A^{12} \\ A^{21} & A^{22} \end{pmatrix}.$$

Then $|A| = |A_{11}|/|A^{22}|$.

Proof.   From the last tableau of the inversion of A, we see that the last pivot element is the reciprocal of the (n, n)-element of A^{-1}.   The next to last pivot element is the reciprocal of the second pivot that we would find in inverting A^{22}, *starting from the bottom and working up*, and so on, thus completing the proof of the theorem.

Theorem 3 enables us to generalize Theorem 4 as follows: Let A_s be the matrix we obtain by deleting from the n-by-n matrix A the rows and columns whose numbers are in a set, s, of integers selected from among the first n integers. Let $A_{\bar{s}}^{-1}$ be the matrix we obtain by deleting from A^{-1} the rows and columns whose numbers are *not* in s. Then $|A| = |A_s|/|A_{\bar{s}}^{-1}|$.

Theorem 5. Adding a multiple of one row of a matrix to another row or a multiple of one column to another column does not change the values of the determinant. Multiplying one row by a constant multiplies the determinant by the same constant.

The proof for rows follows immediately from the definition, except when one row is added to one above it. Theorem 3 enables the reader to complete the proof for this case. Theorem 2 then takes care of the column part of the theorem.

Theorem 5 suggests a geometrical interpretation of a determinant, namely, it is the volume of the parallelepiped determined by the vectors that make up the rows of the matrix. Figure A–1 shows such a "plot" of the matrix

$$M = \begin{pmatrix} 4 & 1 \\ 2 & 4 \end{pmatrix}.$$

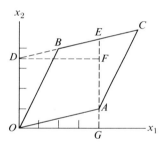

The first row is the vector OA; the second row is OB. The "volume" of this matrix is the area of $OACB$. Subtracting one-half times the first row from the second row does not change the determinant and gives a matrix

$$M^1 = \begin{pmatrix} 4 & 1 \\ 0 & 3.5 \end{pmatrix},$$

Figure A–1

which is plotted by OA and OD. It is clear that $OAED$ has the same area as $OACB$, for ODB and AEC are congruent triangles. Adding a multiple of one row to another, therefore, does not change the volume of the matrix. Subtracting $(1/3.5)$ times the bottom row of M^1 from the first row gives

$$M^{(2)} = \begin{pmatrix} 4 & 0 \\ 0 & 3.5 \end{pmatrix},$$

which corresponds to the rectangle $OGFD$, which clearly has area equal to $|M^{(2)}| = |M^{(1)}| = |M|$. This area is also clearly the same as the area of $OAED$, and therefore the same as that of $OACB$. Hence, $|M| =$ area of $OACB$. An exactly similar argument holds in three dimensions, so it is natural to *define* n-dimensional volumes by determinants.

One may also say that the matrix A *transforms* the unit cube (the identity matrix) into a body with volume $|A|$. One would therefore expect that if transformation of the unit cube by A were followed by transformation by B, the resulting body would have the volume $|A| \cdot |B|$. That is, one expects that $|AB| = |A| \cdot |B|$. And, indeed, we can prove the following theorem.

Theorem 6. If A and B are two square matrices of the same dimension, then $|AB| = |A| \cdot |B|$.

Proof. Performing a row interchange or the row operations described in Theorem 4 on a matrix B amounts to premultiplying B by a matrix obtained by performing the same operation on an identity matrix. Such a matrix is called an *elementary* row matrix. It can be quickly verified from the definition that the determinant of an elementary row matrix corresponding to the interchange of two rows is -1, that corresponding to the addition of a multiple of a row to another is 1, and that corresponding to the multiplication of one row by a constant is that constant. Therefore, Theorems 3 and 4 imply this theorem when A is an elementary matrix. But we know by the Gauss-Jordan process that any nonsingular matrix A is the product of n such elementary matrices, for in the process of inverting A^{-1}, we find $E_1, \ldots E_n$ such that

$$E_n E_{n-1} \cdots E_1 A^{-1} = I.$$

Hence

$$A = E_n E_{n-1} \cdots E_1,$$

and therefore

$$|AB| = |E_n E_{n-1} \cdots E_1 B| = |E_n| \cdot |E_{n-1} \cdots E_1 B| = \cdots$$
$$= |E_n| \cdot |E_{n-1}| \cdots |E_n||B|. \tag{2}$$

When $B = I$, Eq. (2) becomes

$$|A| = |E_n| \cdot |E_{n-1}| \cdots |E_n|. \tag{3}$$

Then, with any B, substituting (3) into (2) gives

$$|AB| = |A| \, |B|.$$

The case of A singular is trivial, for then AB is singular, and by Theorem 1,

$$|AB| = 0 \quad \text{and} \quad 0 = |A| = |A| \, |B|. \quad \text{Q.E.D.}$$

Finally, we come to the theorem responsible for the most widespread and most infelicitous use of determinants, the theorem which connects them with the solution of linear equations.

Theorem 7 (*Kramer's rule*). If A is a nonsingular n-by-n matrix, then the solution of the equations $Ax = b$ can be written

$$x_j = \frac{\sum_{i=1}^{n} (-1)^{i+j} A_{ij} b_i}{|A|} \quad \text{for} \quad j = 1, \ldots, n, \tag{4}$$

where A_{ij} denotes the *determinant* of the $(n - 1)$-order matrix which we obtain from A by deleting its ith row and jth column. The A_{ij} are called the *minors* of $|A|$.

We will prove this theorem in conjunction with the following one:

Theorem 8 (*Expansion by minors*)

$$|A| = \sum_{i=1}^{n} (-1)^{i+j} A_{ij} a_{ij} \qquad \text{for any} \quad j, \tag{5}$$

and

$$|A| = \sum_{j=1}^{n} (-1)^{i-j} A_{ij} a_{ij} \qquad \text{for any} \quad i. \tag{5'}$$

Either of these equations follows from the other by Theorem 2; we can confine our attention to the second.

Theorem 8 can be immediately verified to hold for $n = 2$. Moreover, if Theorem 8 holds for a particular value of n, then so does Theorem 7, as we shall verify by direct substitution. By this substitution, we want to show that with the values of x_i given by Theorem 7,

$$\sum_{j=1}^{n} a_{kj} x_j = b_k \qquad \text{for} \quad k = 1, \ldots, n.$$

But by Eq. (4),

$$\sum_{j=1}^{n} a_{kj} x_j = \frac{\sum_{j=1}^{n} a_{kj} \sum_{i=1}^{n} (-1)^{i+j} A_{ij} b_i}{|A|}$$

$$= \sum_{i=1}^{n} b_i \frac{\sum_{j=1}^{n} (-1)^{i+j} A_{ij} a_{kj}}{|A|} = b_k.$$

The last equality follows because

$$\sum_{j=1}^{n} (-1)^{i+j} A_{ij} a_{kj} = \begin{cases} |A| & \text{if} \quad k = i, \\ 0 & \text{if} \quad k \neq i. \end{cases}$$

In the $(k = i)$-case, the equality follows from Theorem 7. In the $(k \neq i)$-case, Theorem 7 tells us that the expression on the left is the determinant of the matrix in which the kth row and the ith row are the same; Theorem 1 implies that this determinant is zero.

We now prove Theorem 8, and with it Theorem 7, by induction on n. The induction hypothesis, that the theorem holds for $n - 1$, implies, as we have just seen, that Theorem 7 holds for $n - 1$.

It will suffice to show that Eq. (5′) holds for $j = n$, that is, for expansion by the minors of the last row, for if it holds for one value of i, Theorem 3 quickly shows that it holds for any other. Let us therefore partition the n-by-n matrix A as follows:

$$|A| = \begin{vmatrix} B & C \\ d & e \end{vmatrix} = |B|(e - dB^{-1}c),$$

where B is $(n - 1)$ by $(n - 1)$.

Applying Theorem 7 to this $(n - 1)$-order B-matrix, we get the expression $(-1)^{i+j}B_{ji}/|B|$* for the (i, j)-element of B^{-1}. Therefore,

$$|A| = |B| \frac{e|B| - \sum_{i=1}^{n-1} (-1)^i d_i \sum_{j=1}^{n-1} (-1)^j B_{ji}c_j}{|B|}. \tag{6}$$

But by the induction hypothesis,

$$\sum_{j=1}^{n-1} (-1)^j B_{ji}c_j = (-1)^{-n+1} \sum_{j=1}^{n-1} (-1)^{j+(n-1)} B_{ji}c_j$$

$$= (-1)^{-n+1} A_{ni}$$

$$= (-1)^{n-1} A_{ni} = -(-1)^n A_{ni}.$$

Therefore (6) becomes

$$|A| = e|B| + \sum_{i=1}^{n-1} (-1)^{n+i} A_{ni} d_i = \sum_{i=1}^{n} (-1)^{n+i} A_{ni} a_{ni},$$

since $e = a_{nn}$, $d_i = a_{ni}$, and $|B| = A_{nn} = (-1)^{n+n} A_{nn}$.

The induction is accomplished, and both theorems are proved. Those who prefer writing Eq. (4) to writing $x = A^{-1}$ may do so.

---

* The matrix M with $m_{ij} = (-1)^{i+j} B_{ji}$ is called the *adjoint* of B.

INDEX

163

BCDE698